Let me tell you about my friend Roberto Clemente.

A proud Puerto Rican man, Roberto rose up out of poverty and prejudice to become maybe the greatest baseball player of all time. But he was more than a great baseball player; he was a great *human being*. He won all that you could win in the baseball world, including World Series championships, Most Valuable Player awards, and batting titles. He was a fine family man, with a lovely wife and three strong sons. And after eighteen dazzling seasons of major league baseball, Roberto Clemente died a hero.

A Background Note about
ROBERTO CLEMENTE:
The Story of a Champion

This is the story of the extraordinary life of Roberto Clemente, a true American hero, who was born in 1934 and died in 1972 at the age of 38. The story is told by a friend of Clemente's, a man who watched him grow up in Puerto Rico, who witnessed his magnificent baseball career in Pittsburgh, and who volunteered to help during the the feverish efforts to get aid to the victims of the Managua earthquake— the efforts that led to Clemente's tragic death. The man has no name in the story because he stands for the countless thousands of people whose lives were touched by the passion, the excellence, and the sterling character of Roberto Clemente.

Roberto Clemente always spoke proudly of his Puerto Rican heritage. He wanted what success he had to reflect on the people of Puerto Rico. A Puerto Rican journalist said about him, "Clemente was our Jackie Robinson. He was on a crusade to show the American public what a Hispanic man, a black Hispanic man, was capable of." When Clemente won the Most Valuable Player award, it was the first time any Latin player had won the honor in the National League.

"Any time you have an opportunity to make a difference in this world and don't do it, you are wasting your time on this earth."

–Roberto Clemente

ROBERTO

Clemente

THE STORY OF A CHAMPION

JON VOLKMER

TP THE TOWNSEND LIBRARY

ROBERTO CLEMENTE:
The Story of a Champion

TP **THE TOWNSEND LIBRARY**

For more titles in the Townsend Library,
visit our website: **www.townsendpress.com**

Townsend Press, Inc.
439 Kelley Drive
West Berlin, NJ 08091
cs@townsendpress.com

ISBN-13: 978-1-59194-103-3
ISBN-10: 1-59194-103-2

Library of Congress Control Number:
2007943679

Jon Volkmer receives state arts funding support through
a grant from the Pennyslvania Council of the Arts, a state
agency funded by the Commonwealth of Pennsylvania and
the National Endowment for the Arts, a federal agency.

CONTENTS

Chapter 1

Let me tell you about my friend Roberto Clemente. A proud Puerto Rican man, Roberto rose up out of poverty and prejudice to become maybe the greatest baseball player of all time. But he was more than a great baseball player; he was a great *human being*. He won all that you could win in the baseball world, including World Series championships, Most Valuable Player awards, and batting titles. He was a fine family man, with a lovely wife and three strong sons. And after eighteen dazzling seasons of major league baseball, Roberto Clemente died a hero.

In 1972, an earthquake devastated Nicaragua. With typical passion and courage, Roberto took personal charge of getting help to the desperate people. He was aboard a cargo plane he had chartered to carry supplies to help the victims of the earthquake. It crashed just after takeoff. He was only thirty-eight years old.

Less than three months later, a special election made him the first Latin-born player in the Baseball Hall of Fame. Roberto Clemente was *un verdadero hombre*, a real man.

We always knew he was something special. From the time he could walk, he loved baseball. I remember seeing him on the dusty road when he was a little kid, before he even had a regular bat or ball. He would take an old stick, or a guava tree branch, and he would blast crushed-up tin cans halfway across the cane fields. One after another went flying off his bat, and we all stood around, amazed.

It may seem funny that he didn't even have a real bat or ball, but you have to remember this was back in the 1940s, and this was on the island of Puerto Rico. It was, and still is, a part of the United States, but it was very poor. Nobody had any money, except a few of the rich guys who owned the sugar cane farms, and they all lived in San Juan, the capital.

Out where we lived was called Carolina. It had nothing to do with the states like North and South Carolina; that was just its name. These days, Carolina is part of the hustle and bustle of San Juan, but back then it was a sleepy town, way out on the very farthest outskirts. There were some dusty roads, some wooden houses, and a lot of sugar cane fields. The Clementes were better off than most families. They had indoor plumbing. That's because Melchor and Luisa, Roberto's parents, worked hard and brought the kids up right. When Roberto was born, his father was already fifty years old.

There were four other kids and some cousins all living in that small house. But that didn't bother them. They all seemed to get along really well. Melchor could be a hard man; there was no doubt about that. He had started out cutting sugar cane for a living, like his father and grandfather before him. The Clementes' ancestors were Taino Indians and black slaves who were brought from Africa by Spain.

Melchor Clemente worked harder than most. He was smart, too, and he worked his way up to foreman of the Victoria Sugar Mill. That meant long hours and hard work. That was more than a full-time job, but not enough for him. In his time off from the mill, he hauled gravel in a beat-up old truck for local builders.

Melchor worked so hard that Roberto didn't see much of him. Mr. Clemente didn't know about baseball. He didn't have time for fun or sports. But Roberto's brothers played, and they were good. His brother Matino was *very* good. Seven years older than Roberto, he played first base, and rapped out line drives like a machine while his little brother cheered from the grandstand. Matino might have been the first Clemente in the big leagues, but a three-year hitch in the army derailed that dream. Still, Roberto looked up to Matino throughout his whole life, even when Roberto was a star.

That was always a trait of Roberto's, his loyalty. When he was on your side, your family, your team, you could count on him for *anything*. Roberto didn't do things halfway; he was passionate about them. He had a passion for baseball like no one we'd ever seen.

I saw him out in the road one day with a broomstick and a pile of bottle caps. I said, "Momen!" We called him Momen in the neighborhood. I said, "Those bottle caps are awfully small, and so is that broomstick. You'd be lucky to hit one out of ten of them." Momen just gave me that look with those shining eyes and little smile, and *whack*, there went a bottle cap soaring over the road. And *whack whack whack*. One after another, those caps went flying. I swear, he never missed one. You've got to be *good* to hit a bottle cap.

You never saw that kid without a ball. Rubber ball, tennis ball, whatever he had, he'd be throwing it against a wall somewhere, or just throwing it up and catching it. I heard from his momma, Luisa, that he used to drive them crazy at home. Every second he was in the house, he was throwing the ball against a wall. Boom boom boom against the wall. Luisa knew he was special, and she knew he was smart. "You spend too much time with the baseball," she used to tell him. "You should study hard and be an engineer!"

A few years later, when he bought them a new house with his baseball money, Luisa would admit she was wrong. Roberto Clemente was born to play baseball.

But I don't want you to think young Roberto spent all his time playing. Like his father, Roberto was a hard worker. Let me tell you a story. When Roberto was nine years old, he fell in love with a bicycle. Not any particular bicycle, but the *idea* of a bicycle. He could get around so much faster. He could have so much more time to go watch baseball games, so much more time to *play* baseball.

He could hardly contain himself—he was so excited. He waited for his father to come home. His father was late that day, dusty and tired from a long day at the mill. He had not even had dinner yet when Roberto rushed up to him, breathlessly, saying, "Papa, Papa, please buy me a bicycle. I will use it to do more chores, and help out . . ."

"Roberto!" His father cut him off sternly. "What are you thinking? I work two jobs. I can barely keep food on the table and all of you in clothes. Where am I going to get the money for a bicycle for you?"

Roberto turned away quickly, ashamed of himself. It was true. He had brothers and sisters. They all needed basic things just to live and go to school. He should have known better than to ask for a bicycle.

But he did not stay down for long. He announced proudly that he would buy the bicycle himself. One of his brothers laughed at him. "What are you going to do?" he said. "There's no job for a nine-year-old."

But Roberto would not be denied. He found that job. A neighbor of theirs, Senora Martín, wanted someone to get milk for her every day from the store. She had in mind someone older than nine, but Roberto convinced her he could do it. So every morning at six o'clock, Roberto went over and got her milk can. He carried it a half mile to the store and got it filled. It was much heavier on the return trip. I often watched him lugging it along the road. He had to take care not to spill any. But he did the job, every single day, and Senora Martín paid him three cents a day.

Roberto's mother put the pennies in a big glass jar in the kitchen. It seemed to Roberto that they would never add up to enough for a bicycle, but he was determined. He never dipped into that jar to buy anything else, ever. It took him three years, but Roberto saved up $27 and bought himself an almost-new red bicycle. That's just the kind of kid he was.

By the time Roberto was fifteen, he was playing shortstop for an amateur team sponsored by Sello, the rice company. People knew he was special. You see, he could do it all. He could hit like a demon, he had an arm like a cannon, and he was *fast*. The next year he was already in baseball, playing outfield for the Juncos Mules, the top team in the Carolina district. He was in high school then, and he also ran track and field. He could run a fast 440, but with that arm of his, his best event was throwing the javelin. After seeing him throw that spear, some folks were thinking *Olympics*. He was that good.

But as great as he was at track and field, baseball was always Roberto's passion. It didn't take him long to get noticed.

The two top teams in all of Puerto Rico were the San Juan Senadores (the Senators) and the Santurce Cangrejeros (the Crabbers). They both played in Sixto Escobar Stadium, right on the waterfront in San Juan. For American players, Puerto Rico was "Winter League." Since it's warm here year around, the professional players could keep in shape and make some money between seasons up on the mainland.

The major leagues were just starting to become integrated. In 1947, Jackie Robinson became the first black man to play for a major league team, the Brooklyn Dodgers. Robinson was a true hero. He took insults and had threats made against him wherever he went. But he hung in there, and was one of the greatest players of his time—or any time.

Back then, most of the black professional ballplayers still played in the Negro Leagues, and many of the stars came to play in Puerto Rico in the Winter League. There was this one outfielder named Monte Irvin. Two years after Robinson broke the color line, Irvin finally got his chance in the majors with the New York Giants, but he'd been a star in the Negro League for years. He was a graceful outfielder, a black man with a strong arm and good bat who played for the Senadores. Roberto just idolized him.

Melchor could not buy his son a bicycle, but he could give him a quarter to go to see the Senadores. It cost a dime for the bus and fifteen cents to get into the stadium. Roberto was so crazy about seeing the Crabbers, I even gave him a quarter myself once. He was so excited he ran straight for the bus stop. I called out, "Momen, the game doesn't start for two hours!"

"I know," he called back. "I have to see Irvin go in."

And that's what he'd do. Roberto would get there way early just to watch Monte Irvin stride through the crowd up to the stadium entrance. And then, from the stands, Roberto would study every single thing Irvin did, down to how he wiped his hands and how he spat. But mostly he studied how fast Irvin picked up a batted ball and threw it back in. And, sure enough, years later, a lightning-fast throw back to the infield after a hit became Roberto's trademark as a big-leaguer.

Even though Roberto was very shy, eventually Monte Irvin noticed his devoted young fan. They became friends, and Irvin made sure Roberto got in, even when he didn't have money. Irvin would give Roberto his suit bag to carry in, and they'd let Roberto in for free. He was a gentleman, that Monte Irvin.

One good thing about Puerto Rico was that we treated those black ballplayers like gentlemen. Back on the mainland, black players got all kinds of grief. In the South, they couldn't even stay in the same hotels or eat in the same restaurants with the white players. It was just ridiculous. But here in San Juan, we treated them right. Out in Old San Juan, or in the restaurants in Condado, they were celebrities. People crowded around to shake their hands. Restaurants gave them meals on the house. That's the kind of respect Roberto grew up seeing ballplayers get. It's no wonder the racism was so hard on him when he went to the mainland.

Now, we all knew that Roberto Clemente was some special kid, and a very special ballplayer. We knew he could make it big, but even we were surprised at how fast it happened. In October 1952, Roberto was barely eighteen years old. Suddenly he's not watching the Senadores; he's *playing* for the Crabbers, right there in Sixto

Escobar Stadium. He's the youngest guy on the team. We thought, *Wow, Momen is moving up fast.* Then, less than a month later, here comes Al Campanis to San Juan. I mean, *the* Al Campanis, the top scout for the Brooklyn Dodgers. It turns out Campanis was friends with Pedrin Zorrilla, the Big Crab himself, owner of the Crabbers team.

Al Campanis set up a tryout at Sixto Escobar for seventy-two players who dreamed of playing in the big leagues in the United States. Roberto was one of them. They had the recruits throwing and running sprints. I heard that when Campanis saw how fast Roberto flashed through the sixty-yard dash, he said, "If the sonofagun can hold a bat in his hands, I'm gonna sign this guy." That was before Roberto had even picked up a bat. Then Roberto stepped up to the plate and sprayed line drives to every part of the stadium, against top pitching. Campanis' jaw dropped. He sent the other seventy-one players home and continued to be amazed by Roberto's skills. He would say later that Clemente was the best free-agent athlete he had ever seen.

But it was not quite a done deal. It all happened so fast that Roberto's head was spinning. His whole family's heads were spinning. They decided to wait a year before doing anything with the American big leagues. In the meantime, he finished his high school degree and continued to play for the Crabbers. But his fame just kept growing. The word was out about the gazelle-quick outfielder down in San Juan.

Suddenly, a whole slew of major league teams wanted to sign Roberto. The Braves, Dodgers, Cardinals, Giants and Red Sox all said they wanted him. Roberto had a strong desire to go to New York, where he knew there were many Puerto Ricans. Later both the Dodgers and the Giants would move to California, but at this time they were New York teams, along with the legendary Yankees.

The Giants and the Dodgers both tried to get Roberto. As I said earlier, Roberto was an extremely loyal guy. He did not forget that the Big Crab Zorrilla had given him his chance with the Crabbers, and that Al Campanis was the first to spot his potential greatness. Also, Roberto did not forget that it was the Dodgers who had broken the color barrier with Jackie Robinson. He signed with the Dodgers for a $10,000 bonus and a $5,000 first-year salary. It was less than other teams offered, and a lot less than white players were getting at the time, but it was a huge sum for the Clemente family.

And it was New York, and it was the Dodgers.

Little did Roberto know that the Brooklyn Dodgers were not going to show him anywhere near the loyalty and respect that he had showed them.

Chapter 2

The newest ballplayer in the Dodger organization had the kind of body athletes dream of. At nineteen years old, Roberto Clemente stood five feet eleven inches tall, weighed one hundred and seventy-five pounds, and looked like he'd been sculpted out of marble, a rich, dark coffee-colored marble. Back at the tryout, when Al Campanis clocked Roberto's sixty-yard dash on a stopwatch, his time was one half second off the *world record*. Campanis shook the watch as if it was broken, and made Roberto run it again. Same result.

And that never changed. Roberto took himself and his profession seriously. He was never one of those *vida loca* ballplayers, living the wild life. He didn't stay out late, seldom drank alcohol, and watched what he ate. Eighteen seasons and several injuries later, Roberto was still one of the fastest, most graceful outfielders the game had ever seen.

He was a physical wonder with good skills, but that didn't mean he was going to walk right into Ebbets Field, the fabled home of the Brooklyn Dodgers, and start playing alongside Jackie Robinson and Pee Wee Reese. Roberto knew better than that. Big-time baseball doesn't work that way. All the major league teams had minor league teams, called "farm teams," where young players could be developed. So, like Jackie Robinson before him, Roberto would start his career with the Montreal Royals, the Dodgers' top farm club.

First stop, Dodgertown. That's what they called the complex in Vero Beach, Florida, where the Dodgers and their farm teams had spring training. The players and press were calling Roberto Clemente a "bonus baby," because of his contract, and in his first game for the Royals, he showed them what he could do. He knocked in two runs, threw a runner out from the outfield, and, with his amazing speed, pulled off the most exciting play in baseball, an inside-the-park home run. The Royals won 12–2, and the headline read, "Clemente Paces Royals To Win."

In Vero Beach, Roberto also got his first ugly taste of American racism. He was the youngest player on the team, and one of only two black-skinned, Spanish-speaking players. The other was a Cuban shortstop named Chico Fernandez, who was twenty-two. The Dodgers tried to shield those kids from the worst of it. Dodgertown was on land that used to be a naval air station, and it still had that feel, as if it was set off from the rest of the world. The players all lived there and got three meals a day there. But the racism was all around. Every time Roberto left the compound, he saw the signs, "Whites Only" here, "Coloreds Only" there. He couldn't even use the same toilets his white teammates used, much less eat in the same restaurants. He was already lonely for Puerto Rico, where everybody was just another person. The racism made him quiet and bitter.

We didn't know about that part. Back in the Carolina district, we heard what he did in his first game, and we all cheered. We knew it was just the beginning of a great year and a great career. We all said they couldn't keep our Momen down on the farm for long. Pretty soon he'd be called up to the big team, and be playing in Ebbets Field, leading the Dodgers' charge toward the National League pennant.

We were wrong.

A funny thing happened after that first game. Roberto got benched. He hardly got to play in spring ball. And when the team moved up to its home field in Montreal, the same thing happened all over again. He was the standout star of his first game at Delormier Downs, as the Montreal stadium was called. He made great catches in center field. He went three for four batting. The tight game went into extra innings. In the tenth, Roberto put the winning run in scoring position with a sacrifice bunt. He played just as well in the next few games, and then, without explanation, he found himself on the bench again.

And this time he stayed there. For the first time in his life, Roberto was on a team but didn't get to play regularly. He hardly got to play at all.

Montreal was in the International League. There were three teams from Canada and three from New York State, the Rochester Red Wings, the Syracuse Chiefs, and the Buffalo Bison. That year they brought in two teams from farther south, the Richmond Virginians and the Sugar Kings of Havana, Cuba. Those Cubans were crazy for baseball. Back in those days, before Castro took over Cuba, everybody thought there would be a major league team in Havana some day. Just having the Sugar Kings in that league did a lot to help Latin players.

But whether they were at home in Delormier Downs or on the road in Toronto, Ottawa, or one of the New York cities, Roberto Clemente rode the pines. That's what they called sitting on the bench in those days, since the benches were made out of pine.

Back in Puerto Rico, we scoured the newspapers for word of our famous son, our bonus baby, our Roberto, and we couldn't find any mention of him! What happened to Roberto, we all asked each other. Why is Roberto not playing?

If it was hard for us to take, it was much worse for Roberto himself. When they gave him a chance, he usually did well. It's hard to keep your edge and your timing when you don't play, so, sure, he made some strikeouts and a few bad plays. But it was still a mystery why he didn't get to play more.

It went like that for that whole stinking season in Montreal. It was so frustrating for Roberto, passionate Roberto, to be sitting, watching from the dugout, game after game. You might wonder why he didn't make a scene. Why didn't he call up the men in New York who hired him to *play baseball* and demand that he get time on the field?

Well, first of all, you have to remember this was a different era than today. Players were expected to shut up and do what the manager said. The Royals' manager was Max Macon, a respected baseball man who'd been around for years. The youngest player on the team did not confront a seasoned manager, no matter what kind of bonus he'd gotten.

Also, the guys playing ahead of Roberto were not exactly creampuffs. The Royals had a ton of talented outfielders that year, guys like Dick Whitman, who'd won a Purple Heart in the war, getting wounded in the Battle of the Bulge, and

Cuban sensation Sandy Amoros, who had led the International League in hitting the year before. They had powerful Rocky Nelson, who'd belted a record thirty-four homers the previous year. Gino Cimoli and Jack Dempsey Cassini were solid veterans, fighting to make it back to the big club in Brooklyn. What was a shy boy who barely spoke any English and had never played at this level supposed to do?

He kept quiet, bided his time, and did his best on the rare occasions he got to play. He didn't say much to anybody and was known as a loner. Inside, though, the passion for baseball was boiling over in frustration.

Roberto and the Cuban shortstop, Chico Fernandez, lived together in a rooming house near the stadium in Montreal. It was in a French neighborhood; and, unlike Vero Beach, there was no segregation. They went out to eat each day. Chico spoke more English, so Roberto let him do the talking. Every morning they had ham and eggs for breakfast at the same diner. Pretty soon Roberto could say "Ham and eggs!" very well, but he was homesick for his mother's food, and longed to be in his old neighborhood where he knew everyone and people smiled and laughed.

In June, the Montreal Royals traveled to Havana, Cuba, for a series against the Sugar Kings. On the way there, the plane stopped in Richmond, Virginia. Everybody was hungry. Roberto was with a group that headed for a diner down the street from the airport. But Roberto and the other dark-skinned players weren't allowed inside. Imagine what it was like, standing out in the parking lot like stray dogs, waiting for the white players to bring sandwiches out to them. Roberto hated it.

When the Royals landed in Havana, they were *all* welcomed at the luxury Hotel Nacional. But they had only three hours' sleep before a doubleheader at the Havana stadium. Roberto burned to play in front of the Spanish-speaking Cubans. With two games back to back, some of the outfielders would surely need a rest. All the excitement and the Spanish in the air reminded him of Sixto Escobar Stadium back in San Juan. But it turned out to be the same old story. Max Macon looked right through him, as if he wasn't even there. Frustrated, Roberto spent both ends of the doubleheader watching from the dugout.

The Havana trip had one bright spot. Chico Fernandez invited Roberto to his family home for dinner. The sounds of the big happy family, with everybody speaking Spanish, brought tears to Roberto's eyes. He loved the rich smells and tastes of a home-cooked Cuban meal, so much like what he would get at his own home. It was wonderful to be back in the tropics, so close to home. But Roberto did not play in any of the six games in Havana, and when he got on the plane to head back north, he was reminded of how lonely and miserable he was.

As the endless season dragged on, we got word back in Puerto Rico of something we never thought we'd hear, ever. Roberto Clemente wanted to quit. I ran into his brother down by the bus stop, and Matino said it was true. Matino was so mad about what they were doing to his younger brother. His eyes blazed. "Why *shouldn't* he quit?" said Matino. "Momen can play for the Crabbers, make a good living, and be with fans who love him, who appreciate him. Some other big league team will sign him in a second. There's something funny going on up there in Montreal."

Roberto was so angry and depressed that even the Dodgers had to notice. They even sent Al Campanis to talk to him. Campanis spoke Spanish, so here was someone, finally, Roberto could pour out his heart to.

Campanis listened to all Roberto had to say. He looked at the young man kindly. "There's nothing funny going on," Campanis reassured him. "Don't quit now. It's like this for a lot of young players. Have patience. Everything will work out."

Roberto was not happy, but he stayed put in Montreal.

But Al Campanis was not being up front with Roberto. There *was* something funny going on in Montreal—and in Brooklyn. Gradually, with a little help from seasoned players and a few scouts from other teams, Roberto learned what it was.

Yes, there were a lot of good outfielders with the Montreal club that year, which meant there were even better ones, great ones, with the big club in Brooklyn. In fact, with Duke Snider, Jackie Robinson and Carl Furillo, the Dodgers had the best-hitting outfield in the major leagues.

But the rookie from Puerto Rico was good too, good enough to get serious playing time in Montreal, and Max Macon knew it. The Royals' manager was getting the word from upstairs, from Brooklyn, not to play Roberto. Why? The Dodgers were trying to hide him.

Hide Roberto Clemente? From who, from what?

It was all about this new rule in the major leagues. If a club signed a player for more than $4000, and then did not have that player on the big league team's roster at the end of the year, another team could draft him. The team with the worst record got the first pick in that draft. With his bonus, Roberto's pay was well above $4000, so if the 1954 season ended and he was not on the Dodgers' roster, then another team could draft him.

But that team would have to know that he was that good, and the only way they would find out is if they saw him play. If nobody knew about him, then maybe Roberto would be overlooked on draft day, and the Dodgers would get to keep their prize.

When Roberto learned this, he was angry and confused. Sitting around with a couple of the other players one day, he said, "If the Dodgers thought they already had the best outfield in baseball, then why did they act so excited to sign me? I can't believe they want to pay me that much money not to play."

"It's not that much money."

Everyone in the room turned to listen to Joe Black. Joe was a veteran pitcher who rose up through the Negro League and then became a star for the Dodgers. He was down on the farm in Montreal to work his way back from an injury.

"Not that much money," Black repeated. "Even if they never played you, it would be worth every penny just to keep you away from the other guys."

"What other guys?" asked Roberto.

"The team over at the Polo Grounds," Black said, smiling grimly. "I mean the New York Giants. They wanted you too, didn't they, Roberto?"

Roberto admitted that they did.

"They got one fast, flashy outfielder everybody's talking about, Willie Mays. The sportswriters love Mays. If the Giants got our fast, flashy friend here," he teasingly poked Roberto, "nobody might come out to see the Dodgers ever again."

Roberto was stunned to think that the Dodgers would do that, pay all that money just to make sure the Giants didn't get him. But he trusted Joe Black. Inside, he was also wondering what might have been. The Giants not only had Mays; they also had his friend and childhood hero, Monte Irvin. What an outfield that would be, playing with Willie Mays and Monte Irvin!

He must have thought about it a lot that fall. While he rode the pines in Montreal, an exciting pennant race was happening in New York. In the last month the Giants surged ahead of the Dodgers to win the National League pennant. From there they went on to glory, sweeping the Cleveland Indians in the 1954 World Series.

In any case, the Dodgers' attempts to hide Roberto Clemente did not work. The team with the worst record that year, and the first pick in the draft, was the Pittsburgh Pirates. They may have been a bad team, but they had brought in some pretty good baseball minds to turn things around. The general manager was Branch Rickey, the man who, a few years earlier, had made Jackie Robinson a Dodger, breaking the color barrier. Rickey knew the Dodgers and their tricks, and had his scouts keep a close eye on their farm teams. The Dodgers tried to hide Roberto in Montreal, never playing him, but the Pirates were watching.

Even in the limited time of batting practice,

Roberto shone. Angry and frustrated, Roberto stepped up to the plate and blasted balls all over the field. Even playing catch, Roberto threw bullets. He got to play in only 87 games that year, and usually got benched if he made a hit or a good play. His batting average of .257 was nothing special.

But the Pirates knew better. One of their veteran scouts, the dapper Clyde Sukeforth, was a friend of Montreal manager Max Macon. In the cat-and-mouse game, Macon would talk about all his other great players and never mention Roberto. When Sukeforth asked about the kid from Puerto Rico, Macon pretended that Roberto wasn't very good. Sukeforth just smiled. "It looks dead certain we will finish in last place," he said. "And we *will* take Roberto Clemente. Take good care of our boy, will you?"

I always wondered why the Brooklyn Dodgers didn't just put Roberto on the roster at the end of the season. They were no fools. They knew what they had. Roberto's game was a little rough around the edges, but he was going to be a star, and a big one. And the Dodgers knew it. Why mess around with him like that, especially when they could see it wasn't working anyway?

Looking at all the facts, I'm sad to say I think it may have had to do, once again, with the color of Roberto's skin. You see, some people think that after Jackie Robinson broke into the big leagues in 1947, that was the end of racism. The problem had been fixed. A Monte Irvin or a Joe Black could come over from the Negro Leagues and play in the majors. And they did. But racism was still around. Most teams were okay with one or two dark-skinned players, but they seemed nervous about any more than that. Some people have said there was an unofficial quota system.

In 1954 the Brooklyn Dodgers already had a handful of good black players. Besides Robinson, there were Roy Campanella, Jim Gilliam, and Joe Black. Two more, Sandy Amoros and Don Newcombe, were about to become active. That year, the Dodgers might have thought another black player was just too much. That whole season, they seemed to find a reason never to play all their dark-skinned players at the same time. Nobody can prove anything, of course. But everybody agrees that a hot young rookie with Roberto's skills who was white would have gotten a lot more chances to crack the lineup.

The progress against bigotry has been slow. The Boston Red Sox were the last team to integrate, not signing their first black player until 1959. In fact, no major league club would let an all black and Latino team take the field until 1971. That team would be the Pittsburgh Pirates, when Roberto was leading them to a World Series championship for the second time.

Anyway, no man was ever so happy to come

home to our beloved Puerto Rico as Roberto at the end of that miserable 1954 season. Waiting in Puerto Rico were the warm family he loved, the old friends, the food, the music, and baseball. It was time for winter ball! Roberto joyfully pulled on his Santurce Crabbers uniform and ripped into the winter season. He took up his old position in right field, and playing next to him in center was none other than Willie Mays.

We fans were crazy with baseball fever that winter. I went to every game I could, and came home hoarse from screaming. Baseball experts today say it was the best winter ball team ever put together. Besides Willie and Roberto, we had Bob "Big Swish" Thurman in the outfield. Future big-league star Orlando Cepeda was just a kid then. He was on that team too, and so were our Puerto Rican heroes Luis Olmo and Pepe Lucas St. Clair. There was no stopping them.

Willie Mays batted .395 and won the Most Valuable Player award. But our Momen was right there too, hitting .344 and leading the league in hits. The Crabbers took the pennant. They went on to win the Caribbean World Series in Caracas, Venezuela, with Roberto banging out two triples and scoring eight runs.

Pedrin Zorilla, the Big Crab, was never so happy as he was that year. He never had a team like that one.

After the tough time he had in Montreal,

Roberto deserved to forget about everything and just be happy playing baseball. But it was not to be. The Clementes had a family tragedy right in the middle of the winter season. Roberto's oldest half-brother, Luis, was having bad headaches, and then they found out he had a brain tumor. The operation had to be done right away. Roberto took off right after a game, and was driving across the island with his two brothers to be at Luis' side. As they were coming through an intersection, another car came flying in from the side and smashed into them.

Matino and Andres were not hurt, but Roberto wrenched his neck and back so badly he could barely walk. Roberto wasn't thinking about himself, though, and rushed on to the hospital without getting any treatment for his back. The operation came too late for Luis. He died the next day. He was a good man, a schoolteacher. The whole Clemente family was in mourning. And Roberto had got himself a back injury that would plague him for the rest of his life.

Something else happened during that winter ball season. The worst team in baseball, the Pittsburgh Pirates, went to New York for the minor league draft holding the prized number one pick. Without hesitating, they chose Roberto Clemente.

Chapter 3

The Pittsburgh Pirates held spring training at Terry Park, a new stadium and clubhouse in Fort Myers, Florida. Roberto and his new teammates walked around the clean new stadium. They admired how the outfield fences had been set deep, so it was just like the spacious Forbes Field in Pittsburgh.

But Roberto had a sick feeling in his stomach. He was back in the segregated South. This wasn't Dodgertown, where all the players could live and eat together in a closed-off compound. The white Pittsburgh Pirates were given rooms in downtown Fort Myers, at the Bradford Hotel. The black players, including Roberto, were told to find a place to live over in the black neighborhood of Dunbar Heights. Roberto rented a room from a widowed black woman, Etta Power, on Lime Street.

There was no escaping segregation. It was everywhere. When the white players took off for the golf course and the beaches, the blacks were not allowed to go. Even at Terry Park, the big "Whites" and "Colored" signs kept black fans from the best drinking fountains and restrooms. Even the seating was segregated. Black fans were penned up together in one section of the grandstand.

Branch Rickey came to the first intrasquad game in Terry Park. Roberto, standing in a little group with the other black players, was eager to hear encouragement. Branch Rickey would stand up for what was right! And, sure enough, the manager spoke up about the racism in Fort Myers. He said it was damnably wrong. Roberto's heart soared. But as he listened to the rest of Rickey's talk, Roberto's head bent down lower and lower. It became clear that what Rickey wanted most of all was no trouble. Rickey said segregation was just the way it was down there, and there was nothing to be done about it. So all the players were told to be gentlemen, because the people in Fort Myers were nice folks.

At the game, the black fans arrived and dutifully went to their assigned place in the stadium. When he got onto the field, Roberto worked hard to put everything but baseball out of his mind. And once again, he dazzled the fans. His plays in the field caught everyone's attention.

After an amazing shoestring catch on a dead run, the crowd gave him a standing ovation.

The Pirates had been the laughingstock of the league. Suddenly a new buzz was in the air. White Pirate pitcher Bob Friend, who'd suffered the ridicule of fans and sportswriters, knew Roberto was special. He told everyone that a great new talent had arrived. Friend seemed to be inspired by having Roberto on his team. He would go on to have the best season of his life that year, striking out 98 batters and recording a sparkling 2.83 ERA, best in the league.

Roberto was happy to be able, finally, to show what he could do. But Fort Myers made him miserable. He was a proud, dignified man, and he winced at the submissive attitude of the other black players. They said they knew how it was in the South. They accepted it for a chance to play ball. But Roberto could never be like that. When he felt prejudice, he would speak up even when he was urged to be quiet. He said, "I don't want to be treated like a Puerto Rican, or a black, or nothing like that. I want to be treated like any person that comes for a job."

A few rumors started to go around town that the new rookie was talented but "uppity." Roberto didn't care. He didn't know anything about this city called Pittsburgh, but he knew it was up north, and that suited him.

I was working for the American Sugar Company at that time, and I had to travel a lot. Luckily for me, my territory included four National League cities, Cincinnati, Philadelphia, New York, and Pittsburgh. I went to games whenever I could.

I had never cared much about the Pirates. Nobody outside of Pittsburgh did, and even there, not many people cared that much. Very few people could even remember the great Pirate teams of the 1920s. I have to admit I was a little disappointed when Roberto went from Dodgers' "bonus baby" to being a rookie with the lowly Pirates. But I understood that's how the game worked, and at least Roberto would get a chance to play. Whenever my work brought me to Pittsburgh, I always checked in on Roberto to see how he was doing. I'd see a game if the Pirates were at home, and I'd take him out to dinner somewhere on the Hill. That's what they called the black part of town.

Pittsburgh was a big city that was more like a lot of small cities stuck together, with each race having its own area. There were neighborhoods for Italians, Irish, Polish, Jews, and black folks—but not for Puerto Ricans. It seemed that when our people came stateside, they all went to New York.

Roberto was always happy to see me. He was coming along, but his English was still pretty basic. Except for a couple ballplayers, there wasn't anybody to talk Spanish with. When I went back to Puerto Rico, I would bring news of Roberto to family and friends.

The first time I saw Roberto that year, he talked more about rats than about baseball. That old stadium, Forbes Field, it was full of them. Man, he hated them. "I tell you," he said to me, "they are as big as cats. Bigger even!" He told me how the other players teased him about his fear of rats. "They must live with rats all the time where they come from. We may be poor back on the island, but we don't live with rats!"

He didn't have much to say about baseball because he wasn't playing—again. The manager thought he couldn't hit right-handed pitchers. The Pirates started out in typical Pirate fashion, losing their first eight games. When Roberto finally got his first chance, against his old club, the Dodgers, he scratched out an infield hit. It wasn't much, but it was a start.

He was living in the old Webster Hall Hotel, right near the stadium. It was big and looked classy from the outside, but his room was tiny, and the city noise kept him awake at night. Roberto grew up in a peaceful place, and always had a problem with sleeping in big, noisy cities. It hurt his game, being tired all the time. He said his teammates hardly talked to him. I could see in his eyes how lonely he was.

When I came back to Pittsburgh a couple of months later, he was a lot better. There was a nice guy on the team, and a real good pitcher, Bob Friend. Bob lived up to his name. Through Bob, Roberto met another guy, Phil Dorsey. He and Roberto became great friends. They'd hang out together, play cards, go to the movies. Phil had a car. He'd give Roberto rides to the airport for road trips. I was so glad Roberto found a good friend in Pittsburgh.

It was Phil Dorsey who got Roberto out of that noisy hotel. Phil worked for the Post Office, and he had another friend there named Stan Garland. Stan and his wife had a nice brick house in a black neighborhood just up the hill from the stadium. They rented a room to college students sometimes, but they weren't sure about a major league ballplayer. They were upright folks. Mamie Garland made Roberto promise ten times over that there wouldn't be any women or drinking or parties at her house.

Roberto was taken aback. Of course he wasn't like that. They could see that he meant it, and they let him move in. The Garlands were great people. I was invited to eat dinner at their home, and, my, that woman could cook! I was sitting back from that big meal, rubbing my belly, saying what a great cook Mamie was, and how lucky Roberto was to have her cook for him.

They all laughed and told me the story of

how that came about. "When I moved in," said Roberto, "it was just for the room. I ate all of the time in restaurants."

"He was so shy," Mamie Garland said, laughing. "He hardly said a word to us, ever."

"I smelled her cooking every day," said Roberto. "The smell was so good, I thought I was going to pass out." He rolled his eyes upward as if he was going to faint. "I felt like I would trade my arm for just one bite, just one little bite."

"But he never said a word," said Stan. "We thought he wanted to eat out every day."

"So one day I came home," said Mamie, taking up the story, "and I opened the freezer, and it was completely filled with meat. Steaks, roasts, ribs. I was so confused. And then I saw Roberto standing shyly by the door to his room. He put both his hands over his heart, and said, in that cute accent, 'It is all for you. My gift to you for being so kind to me.' Well, I didn't know what to say. It was such a lovely thing to do. But Roberto wasn't finished. He said to me, 'Mrs. Garland, I would like to sit at the table with you, if you don't mind. And if you could make me one of those steaks, I would be very, very happy.'"

We all burst into laughter. "And from that time on," she finished, "when Roberto is in town, he eats his meals here."

I was so happy for Roberto. He missed his family so much, and here was this kind couple who treated him like their own son. Roberto never forgot the Garlands and how they opened up to him when he was the loneliest person in Pittsburgh.

Finally, Roberto was getting to play regularly. He was up and down as a hitter. He'd go on streaks, ripping the ball to left, right and center. Then he'd go for game after game where he'd hit screamers that should have been hits, except they went straight at someone. Roberto would get so frustrated he'd throw down his batter's helmet, hard. He broke a lot of them, and the manager made him pay for them.

Roberto's uniform number was thirteen. When he started hitting all those line drives right at people, being so unlucky so often, other players on the team told him it was that number. So Roberto went to the equipment manager and got a new uniform number. That's how Roberto became number 21, a number he would make famous, wearing it for the rest of his career.

Six weeks into the season, Roberto was looking good. He was hitting .284 with three homers and 16 runs batted in. Sportswriters were beginning to use words like "classy" and "a gem." Roberto's average climbed above .300, and there were whispers in Pittsburgh of the magic words, "Rookie of the Year."

The fans loved his fearless fielding and reckless base running. He caught fly balls in an unusual way, holding the glove at his waist. It was called the "basket catch." Some people thought he was showing off, being a hot dog, and that made Roberto mad. He'd started catching balls that way as a youngster, and he said he could get the ball back in play faster that way. With his rocket arm, he repeatedly gunned down players who dared to try to stretch a single into a double, or a double into a triple.

Roberto added dazzle to the Pittsburgh lineup, but the results weren't much changed from the dreary years before. Before the season was half over, the Pirates were out of the running. Losing was hard on Roberto's spirit, and the way he played was hard on his body.

When I saw him near the end of that long season, he was tired and banged up. His back was still hurting from that car accident back on the island. He had a bruised shin and a sore ankle. He didn't have so many game-winning plays down the stretch, and as he slid, so did the team. They finished last again, with a 60–94 record. By the end of the season, his batting average had shrunk to .255.

The next four years were up and down like that. I was still working at American Sugar, but I didn't make it to Pittsburgh as often. I saw him when I could, and followed the sports pages to see how he and the Pirates were doing.

In 1956 the team managed to climb out of the cellar, barely. They finished next to last instead of last. Roberto was in good spirits that year, though. The Pirates brought in a hitting coach who finally taught him to show some discipline at the plate. Well, a little discipline, anyway. There's a saying that everyone in the Caribbean leagues knows: "Walks don't get you off the island." That means, if you want to get noticed by the big-league scouts, you'd better get hits, not walks. Puerto Rico, Cuba, the Dominican Republic—wherever you are, the players usually swing at almost every pitch, even the ones outside the strike zone.

The crafty pitchers of the major leagues, they take advantage of guys who do that. They throw a bunch of trash up there, anything but a strike, and watch the batters lunge and whiff at unhittable balls. Roberto loved to hit the ball, not watch it go by. He would never be patient enough to take all the walks he could have. But in 1956 he learned to be a little more picky about pitches, and his average climbed right up to .311.

He had some spectacular plays that year. In July, I saw him in a game against the New York Giants. Dusty Rhodes of the Giants sent a drive to right field. Roberto chased the ball, reaching out with his left hand, snagging it, ending the New York rally. Giants outfielder Willie Mays tipped his helmet in Roberto's direction. I read about his hits on July 24, when he had a home run and a triple in a 6–2 drubbing of the Chicago Cubs. Every time Roberto Clemente reached the plate, the ovation grew louder.

And he kept up the hot hitting when he came home to Puerto Rico for winter ball. He always shone when he played at home for us, and that winter he was unbelievable. Momen ran away with the winter league batting championship, hitting a whopping .396.

But the next year was a down year for Roberto. All through 1957 he had injuries. His back bothered him that whole year. The Pirates were bad again, and when they brought in a new manager, Danny Murtaugh, it seemed as if he was looking around for someone to blame. Murtaugh was one of those "tough guys." He thought players should play through injuries, and he questioned if Roberto was really hurt, which made Roberto furious. The sportswriters, too, started saying that Roberto was a baby, that he made up injuries. This hurt Roberto's pride, and he played a lot of games when he should have been sitting out. He ended up having his worst year of his career, hitting just .253 with a paltry 30 RBIs.

But even while the team floundered, the manager complained, and the sportswriters mocked, the fans were growing to love Roberto. You had to be there, in the stands at Forbes Field, to really understand it. There was just something about him. His fine physique in the striking Pirates uniform as he strode onto the field reminded people of royalty. When he came to home plate, he stood far off the plate, legs spread wide, holding the bat high and leaning his muscular upper body over the plate. A wave of excitement would run through the stands. Everybody got the sense that something important was about to happen. Roberto always hustled. His fielding was acrobatic. His outfield arm was like nothing anybody had ever seen. He galloped over large areas of land, grabbing fly balls nobody else could get.

Adding to the excitement was the great play-by-play announcer for the Pirates, Bob Prince. Prince had his own phrase for everything, and the fans just loved it. When a home run was sailing toward the stands, you'd hear Prince calling out, "You can kiss it good-bye!" When a Pirate made a great play, "How sweet it is!" would ring out from the loudspeakers.

Even when the Pirates weren't that good, Bob Prince made the games fun. He had a nickname for every player. Third baseman Don Hoak was "Tiger," and that pudgy catcher, Smoky Burgess, he called "Shake, Rattle and Roll." He had a special one for Roberto. Whenever Clemente came up to the plate, the excited chant would burst over the speakers: "*Arriba! Arriba!*" It is Spanish and means, "Let's go!"

Over the years, Roberto always fought against stereotypes of Hispanics, but he didn't mind when Bob Prince yelled, "*Arriba!*" Roberto knew Prince was not a racist, and he could feel the energy in the stadium at every *Arriba!*

I told you Roberto was a loyal man. Bob Prince was always a big fan of Roberto's, and Roberto liked him back. There was friendship and respect between that announcer and Roberto.

Roberto was even more loyal to the fans, especially the youngest ones. I remember one time after a game at Forbes Field. I was hungry and wanted to make it to a certain restaurant before they closed. Roberto was taking a long time coming from the clubhouse to the parking lot, so I went to find him. When I saw him I called out, "Hey, man, let's go! *Arriba!*"

He looked up, and said, "One moment, please."

And then I saw that he was surrounded by a sea of kids, each one holding up a baseball card or scorecard or scrap of paper for him to sign. And he signed every one, and smiled to the kids, and ruffled their hair. He was so patient, and his eyes were shining.

I felt ashamed of myself for trying to hurry him, and apologized when he came to the car.

"I love the kids," he said simply. "I know what it's like to be there."

I know he was remembering Sixto Escobar,

when he was so shy, and Monte Irvin was nice to him.

In 1958, Roberto had a stint with the U.S. Marine Reserves. He took his training at Parris Island with Platoon 346 of the 3rd Recruit Battalion. That kind of workout seemed good for his back. He was lean and sinewy for the playing season, and the Pirates had added new talent around him. They were a good team that year, and climbed all the way to second place, but still ended up eight games behind the pennant-winning Milwaukee Braves.

That season led to big hopes for 1959, but once again nagging injuries bothered Roberto, and the Pirates slipped to fourth place.

After five years in the major leagues, Roberto Clemente had played some sparkling baseball. But a lot of people were saying that he had not lived up to the potential of the kid who was the "bonus baby" and first pick in the minor league draft. Some were even saying he was a bust. He was twenty-five years old. Injuries had kept him off the field for a lot of games, and slowed him down for a lot more. He was handsome as a movie star and had a body that looked as if it could have been shaped by Michelangelo. But Pittsburgh had brought him there to win a National League pennant, and to compete in the World Series. Given the marvelous potential that so many experts saw in him, Roberto was considered a disappointment.

All that was about to change.

Chapter 4

Roberto got a new contact at the beginning of the 1960 season. At $27,500, plus bonuses, it was not exactly generous. Roberto signed it, but he wrote a letter to the general manager, Joe Brown. He showed me a copy of it later. In it he explained that he played hurt most of the last season, and nobody had listened to him. He'd made quite a few errors in the field the year before, but he did not apologize for that. He calmly defended his all-out play. If everyone played it safe all the time, he wrote, then it would be easy never to make an error.

Having cleared the air, Roberto got down to business. He still had back pain, but overall he felt pretty good that year. The rest of the team was feeling good too. Quietly, the Pirates had made some shrewd trades and added some quality players over the last few years. They were ready to contend for a championship.

In the home opener against the Cincinnati Reds, excitement was in the air. A sellout crowd watched their heroes take the field. Roberto asserted his leadership right off. He had two doubles, a single, and a long sacrifice fly, leading the Pirates to an easy 13–0 victory. In an Easter Sunday double-header against the Reds, Roberto spearheaded a 5–0 victory with a two-run homer. Within a week, the Pirates had an unheard-of nine-game winning streak going, and Roberto was the driving force.

He kept it going. In May he was named the National League's Player of the Month, with a .336 average and 39 hits and 25 RBIs in 27 games. Suddenly, people were noticing Roberto. Stan Musial called him a fine player, and the old-timers were starting to compare him to the greats like Joe DiMaggio.

But it wasn't easy for Roberto. The sports-writers could be a real pain, pointing out every flaw, and stirring up trouble between teammates. They never gave him enough credit for what he did to make the Pirates winners, and they twisted his words around. When Roberto said he was a Puerto Rican, and that he was not like the other black people in Pittsburgh, the writers turned that around to say he didn't like black people. He didn't mean that at all. He especially hated it when they wrote out his accent, making him sound foolish, quoting him saying things like,

"Eet ees beeg games for us thees week."

But in spite of all that, something special was happening that season for Roberto and for the team. You could feel it in the air. I went to several games that summer, and there was magic. In addition to playing sharp baseball, the Pirates were getting the good bounces too. When they were desperate for a hit, someone would manage a bloop single, or rap out a seeing-eye hit just out of the reach of a lunging shortstop. When they needed a big play in the field, there was Roberto, gunning down a runner from right field. The pitchers came through in the clutch. Everybody was hitting. Roberto would come up to bat, we'd hear "*Arriba! Arriba!*"—and the whole stadium would go wild.

The Pirates were finally in first place, but they didn't run away with the pennant. The Milwaukee Braves and the St. Louis Cardinals kept up the chase, putting pressure on the Pirates all year long. As the season drew to a close, it came down to the Pirates and the Cardinals. Finally, on September 25, the Pirates were in Milwaukee, in the middle of a tough game, when word came over the loudspeakers that it didn't matter who won. Fifty miles south, in Chicago, the Cubs had beaten the Cards, knocking them out of the race. The Pirates had won the National League pennant!

Roberto did everything that season. He hit .314, had 94 RBIs, and his incredible, spirited play had revitalized the whole team. The most important thing to Roberto—I remember it brought tears to his eyes—was that he, the only black member of the team, was voted by the fans as their favorite player.

There was not much time to celebrate, as the mighty New York Yankees awaited them in the World Series. The pennant fever changed into nervousness as the Pittsburgh fans faced the facts. The Yankees had walked away with the American League pennant, finishing eight games ahead of Baltimore. Mickey Mantle was hitting home runs over the roof at some stadiums, and the Yankees had brought in a young slugger to hit behind him, named Roger Maris. Mantle and Maris were so good they were being compared to the famed "Murderer's Row" lineup of the 1927 Yankees that had Babe Ruth and Lou Gehrig. In Las Vegas, the smart money was on the Yankees, easy favorites over the upstart Pirates.

Roberto had his own problems. He'd cut his face badly smashing into a concrete wall chasing down a fly ball against the Giants. He'd lost 20 pounds off his already lean frame during the season, and he was tired. As usual he had his aches and pains. But now he had to be the David against a Goliath in pinstripes.

He had grown to love Pittsburgh and its fans. They deserved a World Series crown. Roberto put aside his anger at the sportswriters who underrated him. He forgot all his nagging injuries and his body's weariness. He just wanted to win.

It turned out to be the wildest, most exciting World Series ever played.

In those days, the National League and American League took turns being the home team. So even though they had a better record and were the favorite, the Yankees came into Forbes Field as the visitors in the first game. A noisy sellout crowd of 36,676 was waiting for them.

I was at that game, and, for once, I was not the only Puerto Rican in the crowd. Many people had flown up from the island, including Roberto's mother and his brother Matino. Roberto got us good seats. We had our own Momen Clemente cheering section, and he gave us plenty to cheer about.

In the bottom of the first inning, the Yankees' pitcher, 15-game winner Art Dittmer, got his first taste of National League power. The Pirates had already scored two runs when Roberto came up with a man on base. As smooth as silk, Roberto stroked a single up the middle, bringing in another run. That was it for Dittmer. There was a pause in the game as the Yankees brought in a new guy. We were going crazy in the stands. The awesome Yankees? The terrifying Yankees? Our Roberto had chased their ace out of the game after only 18 pitches.

There was one play that scared us all to death.

In the fourth inning, the Yankees' Yogi Berra smashed a ball to deep left-center. We watched in horror as Roberto and centerfielder Bill Virdon sprinted at top speed toward the exact same spot. Both of them were calling for the ball, but in the roar of the crowd, neither one could hear. We all held our breath. It looked like certain disaster. As the two players came together, at the last second Roberto somehow managed to pull off, wrenching his body sideways, allowing the leaping center fielder to make a beautiful catch. Everyone in the stadium let out a wild cheer—and a huge sigh of relief.

The Pirates went on to win, 6–4, and we were flying high. We knew we had the Yankees on the run.

But the Yankees had other ideas, and the second game brought us crashing back to earth. It started out pretty well. Bob Friend had good stuff. He threw six strikeouts in four innings. The Pirates were behind 3–0, but it didn't seem that bad. The Pirate bats could bring them back. A lot of us fans thought the Pirate manager, Danny Murtaugh, panicked a bit, pulling Friend for a pitch-hitter in the bottom of the fourth.

It turned out to be a real bad move, as the Yankees jumped all over the Pirate relievers. That game got ugly fast. The Yankees pounded out 16 runs on 19 hits. Roberto had two hits, but Mickey Mantle had two home runs. The final score was

16–3, but it seemed even worse than that.

The series moved to the Bronx for the next three games, and everybody in New York thought it would end there. New York fans said the first game had been a fluke. The second game showed how the two teams really stacked up. It looked as if they were right in Game 3. After one inning it was 6–0 Yankees. Their great pitcher Whitey Ford threw a complete game shut-out, and the Yankee bats continued to sing. Final: 10–0 Yankees.

But once again, just as it seemed the Pirates were about to be run out of the World Series, they came back with not one but two gritty wins in Yankee Stadium. With magnificent pitching and just enough hitting, they edged the Bronx Bombers by scores of 3–2 and 5–2.

While everyone was cheering the great Pirate pitching, a few people were noticing another star. An Associated Press sportswriter penned an article about Roberto titled "The Unsung Hero of the World Series?" The article pointed out how Roberto's incredible arm in right field had held the Yankee runners pinned down on the bases, helping Pittsburgh to each of its three wins.

Back in Pittsburgh for Game 6, the Yankees once again let out their frustrations, crushing the Pirates 12–0.

This was a strange World Series. The Yankees had destroyed the Pirates in their three wins by a combined score of 38–3. And yet the series was tied 3–3. Our Pirates were at home, and we liked their chances. The Yankees were pumping out hits and runs, but they had used up their hottest pitcher. Whitey Ford had thrown his second complete game shutout in Game 6. Meanwhile, the Pirates had *their* ace, Vernon Law, rested and ready to go.

What followed was one of the greatest games in World Series history.

Game 7 began well for the Pirates. Roberto's old friend from the Montreal Royals, Rocky Nelson, got a rare start at first base. Rocky responded with a two-run homer in the first inning. The Pirates tacked on two more in the second, and all of us in the stands were starting to believe we were about to win it all. *This is it. We're going to beat the Yankees!*

But the game was far from over. The Yankees fought back behind a Yogi Berra home run, and suddenly it was the bottom of the eighth with the Pirates down 7–4. The Pirates seemed doomed. They had come so far. It seemed tragic to go down now.

Then came a strange piece of luck for the Pirates, even as it was terrible luck for the Yankee shortstop Tony Kubek. On what looked like a routine double-play grounder, the hard-hit ball took a crazy bounce and caught Kubek square in the throat. The shortstop was laid out flat. He did get up, but he was spitting blood and had to be taken to the hospital with a bruised larynx. The inning went on.

The Pirates had scored one run, and had two men on base when Roberto came up with two outs. He had been hitless in three at-bats so far in the game. The Yankee pitcher, Jim Coates, was a crafty veteran who knew Roberto liked to swing the bat. He wasn't about to give Roberto anything good to hit. He threw every pitch way outside, out of the strike zone. Sure enough, Roberto could not lay off. Roberto was swinging at everything, but he kept catching a piece of the ball, fouling off one pitch after another.

Coates threw outside again, and Roberto went fishing again. This time the pitcher got what he wanted, a slow roller down the first base side. Everyone in the park groaned. Another out for Roberto. Or was it? Roberto ran like the wind. With the first baseman fielding the hit, it was Coates's job to cover first. He got there, but Roberto got there first, beating out an amazing infield single and bringing home a run. That brought the Pirates to within one, 7–6.

The next batter was Hal Smith. The stadium buzzed with excitement. Out on the streets and in the houses of Pittsburgh, everyone was glued to a television or radio. The Pirates were coming back from the dead! Smith was not even a starter. He was a backup catcher and no great hitter, but it didn't matter. This was a year of destiny. He smashed a home run to put the Pirates ahead 9–7.

Now it was our turn. Only three more outs and the Pirates were the world champions! But the Yankees would not go quietly. They battled back, tying the game in the top of the ninth with Mickey Mantle leading the way.

In the bottom of the ninth, with the score tied 9–9, the first batter up was Bill Mazeroski. He was a brilliant-fielding second baseman. Bob Prince's nickname for him was simply The Glove. He'd had a good year at the plate, too, hitting .273 and knocking in 64 runs. He was not known at a power hitter, but this was a magic year. We all stood and cheered as The Glove stepped up to the plate. Mazeroski responded. He took the second pitch he saw and blasted it over the left field fence. By the time he got to second, he was dancing and throwing his helmet in the air. By the time he got to third, the fans were pouring onto the field. By the time he pounced on home plate, the whole Pirate team was waiting for him, and Forbes Field was bedlam.

A walk-off home run in the bottom of the ninth of the seventh game of the World Series. The Pittsburgh Pirates were the world champions. The team, and the city, went crazy with joy. *How sweet it is!* Bob Prince would say.

What about Roberto? He had done his part, hitting .310 for the series and being the only

Pirate to hit safely in every game. And yet he was subdued after the win. While the players screamed and doused each other with champagne, he quietly showered, packed his bag, and got ready to leave.

One of his teammates yelled, "See you at the victory party tonight, right, Roberto?"

Roberto just shrugged. He didn't like those wild parties. He felt out of place and awkward. "I catch a plane tonight for New York," he said. After winning the World Series, Roberto Clemente was ready to come home and enjoy his victory his way, quietly, with the people he loved.

When he stepped out of the clubhouse door, the reaction caught him by surprise. A huge crowd swallowed him up, chanting his name, pounding him on the back, begging for autographs. I was there and saw it first-hand. Roberto's shock quickly turned to joy. It took him nearly an hour to get to the parking lot, and he loved every minute of it. His eyes were shining. He clutched his bag in one hand and in the other a box containing the trophy he was so proud of, from when he was voted the fans' favorite Pirate.

If the Pittsburgh fans loved him, the people of Puerto Rico were ready to crown him king. From the moment his plane touched down in San Juan, cheering crowds followed him everywhere. They had listened to every pitch of the World Series, followed his every throw and hit. We held banquets for him and gave him trophies.

Roberto should have been on top of the world. But then something happened to remind him that back in the mainland, despite all he'd done, he was still a dark-skinned, funny-talking foreigner.

The National League Most Valuable Player award was announced. The winner was Dick Groat, Roberto's teammate. Groat had led the league in batting average at .325, a few points ahead of Roberto's .314. But Groat had only two home runs and a measly 50 RBIs. Roberto had 16 home runs and 94 RBIs. Plus Groat had been out with injuries several weeks during the season, while Roberto had played through pain.

Roberto was not mad at Groat. He respected his teammate. To be edged out by the shortstop was something Roberto could take. But he was not edged out; he was humiliated. Roberto was not second in the voting, or third. He wasn't even fourth or fifth. He was *eighth*. Ahead of him were two more Pirates, Don Hoak and Vernon Law, and five players from other teams.

Eighth?

Back when Roberto was just a rookie player, a sportswriter asked him if he wore a loincloth back home in Puerto Rico. Another called him the "chocolate-covered islander." These things Roberto never forgot. The MVP snub was just more evidence that he had yet to get his due as one of the best players of the game. Racism was still rampant. In quiet protest, he refused to wear his World Series championship ring.

Chapter 5

The magic of 1960 wasn't there the following year, or for many years after. As a team, the Pittsburgh Pirates slumped back into their doormat role. As a player, Roberto just kept getting better. On July 10, 1961, Roberto was hitting for power and sporting a glittering .357 average, and was voted a starter in the All-Star Game at Candlestick Park in San Francisco. He was outstanding in the game and was voted the Most Valuable Player for the All-Star Game. The Pirates ended the season with a losing record, but Roberto's .351 average won him the silver bat as the National League's top hitter, the first of four times he'd win the batting title. He also won the first of *twelve straight* Gold Gloves as one of the league's top three outfielders.

His numbers were down a bit in 1963, a year when his injuries were bothering him. Once again he had to put up with more sportswriters accusing him of making them up. Still, he hit .312 for a last-place team.

In the winter of 1963, twenty-nine-year-old Roberto was still unmarried. It wasn't that he was a loner, as he was those first years back in Pittsburgh. In San Juan he was much more at ease, and, after all, he was the island's biggest celebrity. We would see him and his friends at the hot clubs in San Juan. There were always pretty girls around, and they all wanted to be Mrs. Clemente. And why not? Not only was he a beautiful man with a body like a god, but he was a real gentleman, always polite. And he was very rich, by our island standards anyway.

Still, Roberto did not take advantage of this star status. He respected the traditional ways. One time, for example, Roberto kept a girl out on a date an hour later than he had promised her father to return her home. To avoid a scolding from her father, he pretended the car had run out of gas. He and a friend pushed the car the last few yards to try to make it look as if it really happened.

Roberto did not want any of those flashy girls. He was a quiet person who never liked the wild nightlife. The woman he married would be the same sort of person, someone with whom he could create a warm and loving home where he would spend most of his time.

In December 1963, a girl with brilliant dark

hair and vivid brown eyes was on her way to her parents' home. She was twenty-two-year-old Vera Cristina Zabala, secretary for the local government bank. She was riding with her brother when they met a white Cadillac going in the other direction. Vera Zabala saw that the man driving the white Cadillac was the baseball star Roberto Clemente. Of course she knew what he looked like. His picture was in the newspaper every day.

She knew about him but had never seen him play baseball. A graduate of the University of Puerto Rico, Vera had coffee-colored skin and a warm personality. She was shy, and she expected her life would play out in an ordinary way. In her wildest dreams she never expected, as she said, "to be married to a famous person, and to be traveling and talking to so many people." When she caught that glimpse of the great Roberto Clemente she thought it was interesting, but she didn't go crazy like a giggling young girl.

The second time the paths of Vera Zabala and Roberto Clemente crossed, it was Roberto who noticed her. And he noticed her in a big way. He saw her on the street, heading into a drugstore. He was transfixed. He parked his car and went into the drugstore. He stood around pretending not to watch while she picked up a few things, paid for them, and left. He went straight to the clerk and asked if he knew who she was. The clerk was wary about saying too much. He knew her father was a strict man who was suspicious of young men paying attention to his daughter.

Roberto didn't let that stop him. He asked around until he found someone willing to introduce him to the Zabalas. You see, that's how it was in Puerto Rico in those days. We were respectful. Even a superstar baseball player couldn't just walk up to a single girl on the street and start talking. If it was going to go anywhere, it had to be done right, through family channels.

A high school teacher who lived near the Zabala house also knew Roberto. He told Vera that Roberto was interested in her. She said she would think it over. The family was suspicious. What did the big baseball star want with Vera? Maybe his intentions were not honorable. It was bewildering to her and her family that such a well-known man wanted to see her.

After some time of being put off, poor Roberto was going crazy. He did not want to seem too forward, but he was very anxious to meet Vera. She seemed to him the perfect girl. To help him out, the same high school teacher invited Vera Zabala to a baseball game where Clemente was playing. Afterwards they would all gather at the teacher's house for refreshments. It was very proper, but the plan went awry. Before Roberto could get to know Vera, her brother swooped in and took his sister home. Roberto did not give up. He called Vera and invited her to lunch. She refused. He called her again, and this time she agreed to meet him.

During lunch, Roberto asked to meet Vera's parents. She told him her parents were very strict and she could not ask him to her house. Vera Zabala's father laid out rigid rules for any dates his daughter had. He told her how many days she could see a young man each week and how many hours she could spend with him.

The next day Vera received a beautiful bouquet of flowers at her bank job. A few more lunches followed, and then Roberto presented Vera with a ring. She gasped, "I don't even know you." Roberto was sure, and Roberto was determined. He pleaded once again for the chance to meet her parents. Finally she relented.

When Roberto arrived at the Zabala house, he discovered Vera's father and his father, Melchor, knew each other. He hoped that fact would break the ice for him with Vera's father. It did not. Vera's father had a blunt question for the baseball superstar. What was he doing here? What did he want with Vera, a middle-class girl? Surely a rich and famous star athlete could find girls from finer backgrounds than Vera. Roberto said in reply, "I can walk down to the corner and probably get ten girls. But I don't care. The one I love is here."

Vera and Roberto began dating. When Roberto returned to Florida for the 1964 spring training season, he wrote daily letters to Vera. Roberto had become a leader in the Pirate clubhouse and among all players in the National League. He was a mentor to younger Caribbean players who were deeply grateful for his help. Roberto remembered being a Spanish-speaking young man in the strange white world of major league baseball himself, and he wanted the journey to be less painful for the Latin players coming up.

Roberto always felt a lot of pressure to succeed on the field. In his free time, he avoided the party scene. He preferred to spend his free time with family and close friends. He liked the fans. The children were his favorites. But he was wary of strangers, especially of sportswriters who were not always on his side. Roberto also loved to spend time with ordinary people—in Puerto Rico and in Pittsburgh. He enjoyed talking to elderly people, taxi drivers, the poor, and the underdogs. He felt more at home with them.

During the first half of the 1964 season, Roberto phoned Vera from Pittsburgh and from every road trip city. He was eager to get married. He was thirty years old, and it was time for him to marry, settle down and raise a family.

In July, Vera Zabala and her mother came to New York to see Roberto play in the All-Star Game. He was leading the league with a .345 average. He started in right field, scoring and helping the National League to a 7–4 win. Luisa

Clemente, Roberto's mother, was also there. She had seen her son play in the World Series, but this was her first All-Star Game.

Right after the All-Star Game, Roberto had to return to Pittsburgh for a game against the Cincinnati Reds the next night. He made sure his guests, the Zabalas and his mother, were well taken care of in Pittsburgh. He asked the Garlands to let them have his rooms at the house where he lived, and he rented an apartment for himself for the week. The Garlands showed such kindness to the Zabalas that it helped Roberto prove his worthiness to take Vera as his wife.

Vera was deeply touched by how thoughtful Roberto was, and she knew now that she wanted to marry him. It dawned on her during the All-Star Game what a famous man he really was, and yet he was so down-to-earth and untouched by his own celebrity that she was amazed. Roberto presented Vera with two more engagement gifts—a pearl necklace and a watch. The wedding would be in November.

As a team, the Pittsburgh Pirates were floundering again in 1964. After 1960, the best reason to come to any Pirates game was just to see Roberto play. The team wasn't good, but he was great. He was the show in Pittsburgh. Seeing him running, hitting, making catches, firing balls from the outfield—that was enough to bring fans to the stadium. Roberto finished the season with a .339 batting average, rapping out 211 hits and winning himself another batting title.

I have never seen anything like what happened on November 14, 1964. Thousands of my countrymen lined the streets for the great occasion, the wedding procession of Vera Zabala and Roberto Clemente. Only three hundred would fit in San Fernando Church, and I was lucky enough to be invited.

The most famous son of Puerto Rico was taking a wife, and it was a grand occasion. He had gone north to the United States and been swallowed up in the strange world of major league baseball. He might have remained there and married a North American girl and rarely if ever come home. But that was not Roberto Clemente. He had the heart of a Puerto Rican, and he never forgot his roots. The wedding would be here near where he grew up, where he played baseball as a child with an old sock for a ball and a broomstick for a bat.

The governor of Puerto Rico was there, and so was the general manager of the Pirates. Howie Haak, one of the scouts who helped snatch Roberto from the Dodgers, was there. Close friends were there. Roberto never forgot old friends. I waved to his adopted parents, the Garlands. I went over to shake their hands and saw Roberto's old pal Phil Dorsey was with them. It was great to see him there too. And ballplayers! There were enough to start winter ball. And then the Clemente family, parents Melchor and Luisa, brothers Matino, Osvaldo, and Andres.

Roberto looked nervous up there, turning his head from side to side, the way he did when he was walking up to the plate. With his body and face, Roberto would look good in a sugar sack. He made the Pirates uniform look princely. But he never looked so good as he did on his wedding day. He wore a black tuxedo, and it fit him to a T.

Flor Manuel Zabala, the stern father Roberto had to win over, escorted his daughter down the aisle. Vera Zabala had a gown of Italian silk satin, with sleeves embroidered in white porcelain beads and tiny pearls.

As the bride and groom stood before Father Salvador Planas for the vows, we were all dead quiet. Roberto's soft tenor voice came clearly through the church, as he said *Acepto*. Yes, he did take Vera Zabala to be his lawfully wedded wife.

Joyful music filled the church and thousands roared their approval as the couple came out after the ceremony. The Clementes honeymooned in the Virgin Islands and then spent the Christmas season visiting the Clemente and Zabala family homes.

With his World Series money, Roberto had fulfilled a dream he had all his life, to buy his mother a new, fine home. Now, four years later, he bought a beautiful home in which to raise his own family, a villa atop a large hill with a beautiful view of San Juan Bay. Vera soon learned that her husband enjoyed nothing so much as being home. He did not care much for parties, and he did not want to hang out with old friends. He wanted to be home, tinkering with family appliances, clearing away brush, mowing the lawn.

When Roberto was not puttering around the house, he was spending time with his hobbies. He played the harmonica and the Hammond organ. He enjoyed popular music and hymns for church. He made pottery, and he learned to paint china and make lamps. Home was Roberto's haven, and he went there as often as he could.

Sometimes Roberto's yard work got him in trouble. While he was mowing his lawn one day, a rock shot from the machinery of the mower, hitting him in his upper right thigh near the hip. Roberto was taken to the hospital when the wound swelled and it had to be drained.

While he was recovering from that operation, Roberto was busy organizing a series of games to show off Caribbean baseball talent. The best of Puerto Rico and Cuba would take on the Dominican stars in Santo Domingo, the capital of the Dominican Republic. Roberto wasn't feeling well. He was running a fever and feeling weak and sick all the time. Roberto played in the outfield, but he was feeling very bad. The Dominicans, led by the Alou brothers, Felipe, Mateo, and Jesus, took two out of three in the series.

He came back home to Puerto Rico, but continued to get worse. At times he was delirious. A frightened Vera called for help, and he was taken to the hospital. Finally the correct diagnosis was made. Roberto had malaria.

Late in March, the fever broke at last, and Roberto started to get better. He tried to get himself back to health quickly by relying on his famous milkshakes. He loved fruit, and he believed it had powerful health-giving properties. He made milkshakes out of strange combinations: orange juice, mashed pears and peaches, egg yolks, bananas, and ice cream.

When 1965 spring training camp began in Florida, Roberto was there. He looked too thin and weak, but he amazed his teammates by hitting with his usual power. Still, Roberto lacked his old stamina. He did not get off to a good start in batting that year, and in mid-May his average was a meager .243. But those milkshakes must have done their job, because suddenly Roberto was on fire, and his average shot up like a thermometer on a hot day. As the season neared the All-Star break, Roberto passed Willie Mays for the National League's batting lead, and was hitting a torrid .338.

Roberto played in the All-Star Game and continued his amazing hitting for the rest of the summer. Riding Roberto's bat, the Pirates climbed to a respectable third-place finish in the National League, seven games behind the Dodgers.

Even more encouraging was that there was a new rising star in the Pirate lineup, a young African-American slugger named Willie Stargell. Willie had joined the team at the very end of the 1962 season, and was making a name for himself with his bat. Roberto was one of the greatest hitters the game had ever seen, but he was not a power hitter. He had averaged under ten home runs a year in his first decade of major league ball. Willie Stargell had the power, and his home run totals were climbing the charts, from 21 in 1964, to 27 in 1965. He would hit 33 dingers in 1966. This was a great sign for the future of the Pirates, who would eventually ride the bats of Roberto, Stargell, and other new stars to a second World Series championship.

Meanwhile, in 1965, Roberto earned his third National League hitting crown. In doing so he became only the fifth player in National League history to claim at least three batting titles, joining Rogers Hornsby, Stan Musial, Honus Wagner and Paul Waner. His salary for 1965 had risen to $70,000. Not only would he play for the Pirates, but he had a new job as well. He was supposed to scout new Puerto Rican talent during the winter baseball season.

Roberto's plays continued to draw awe. In a

game against the Houston Astros, Roberto raced across the outfield after a ball, dove headfirst, and scooped up the ball with his glove. On his knees, his face covered with dirt, Roberto fired to third base to retire the lead Astro runner.

For all that he accomplished on the field, the greatest thing that happened to Roberto in 1965 had nothing to do with baseball. Vera Clemente was pregnant. They had a nice place in Pittsburgh, but Roberto was adamant that she should return to Puerto Rico to have their child. He wanted his children to be born in Puerto Rico and nowhere else. Roberto Clemente, Jr., was born in Santurce, Puerto Rico on August 17, 1965. For both Vera and Roberto, it was a wonderful blessing. They both wanted children. and little Roberto was a beautiful, healthy boy. Now they were a real family.

After the season Roberto returned to Puerto Rico for the winter. The house on the hill at *Rio Piedras* was furnished the way the Clementes liked it. There were moat-like ponds and Aztec symbols. There were three large bedrooms and room to subdivide them as more children came. The neighbors were doctors, engineers—all professional people. Best of all, living nearby were Vera's parents and Roberto's parents, so the families could get together frequently.

Roberto had a fine winter playing with his baby son, and finding more do-it-yourself projects around the house. And it was during this winter that the great dream took root in his mind and heart. He was very much aware of how fortunate he was. His amazing baseball gifts had brought him and his family wealth and security. But he looked around and saw so many little children without any opportunities at all.

He remembered his own childhood when he played baseball with tree branches and soup cans. But there were more problems now. When Roberto grew up, it was a more innocent time. Now there were so many more opportunities for young people to get into trouble. Thousands of poor Puerto Rican children with both parents working for low-paying jobs roamed around with nowhere to go for recreation. Roberto wanted to build a sports city for them, a place where children could play baseball and basketball, swim, and enjoy their childhood in a safe environment.

Roberto knew his dream would cost a lot of money. He was wealthy by Puerto Rican standards, but even he could not afford it all by himself. The government would have to help.

In his spare time, Roberto wandered around San Juan looking at empty tracts of land. He envisioned a sports city close to all the poor neighborhoods so the city kids could walk to it.

When his baseball career ended, Roberto thought he would like to work with kids all the time. He imagined himself doing for other youngsters what older mentors had done for him.

All these youngsters would not turn into baseball superstars, but they would gain confidence in themselves. They would have a chance to dream their own dreams.

Chapter 6

1966 was a good year for the Pittsburgh Pirates. They started hot, winning 13 of their first 19 games. Vera remained in Puerto Rico awaiting the birth of their second child. Luis Roberto was born July 13, 1966. Roberto was acting like a father figure to his younger teammates, too. The Pirates had picked up two Dominican players who would become future All-Stars. One was the best of the Alou brothers, Mateo, known at Matty, and the other was Manny Mota.

Roberto remembered what it was like to be the guy who didn't know anyone and spoke only Spanish. He took the younger players under his wing. With Roberto's help, Matty had a break-out year, transforming from a so-so pull hitter to a very good spray hitter. The year before with the Giants, Matty Alou hit an anemic .231. In his first year with the Pirates, his average went up over 100 points, to a league-leading .342. With Matty

Alou lining up in the outfield with Roberto and Willie Stargell, suddenly the Pirates had a lineup to make other pitchers afraid.

Roberto was having a good year too, maybe the best of his career. He was never a big home run hitter, but 1966 proved an exception. His manager came up to him and said, "Roberto, you're a great hitter. But we need more power from you. We need more home runs if we're going to win." Roberto responded to the challenge. He crushed a career-high 29 dingers that year, including some towering shots that left fans gasping, and batted in 119 runs, also the most of his career.

Meanwhile, he had secured his place as the most feared right fielder in the game. Nobody ran on Roberto's arm. The sportscaster Vin Scully was hardly exaggerating when he said, "Clemente could field the ball in New York and throw the guy out Pennsylvania."

Roberto again earned a spot in the All-Star Game. His National League teammate and starting pitcher was the Dodgers' ace, Sandy Koufax. It was 105 degrees in St. Louis that day. Fans were passing out in the stands at brand-new Busch Stadium, and everyone groaned when the game went into extra innings. Roberto wasn't fazed by the heat. He had a key single in the 2–1 National League victory.

I didn't see too many games that year, but I will never forget one at Wrigley Field in Chicago. The Pirates were locked in a pennant race, and there was a thrill in the air. They were nursing a 1–0 lead in the fifth when Roberto stepped up to the plate with two men on against Ferguson Jenkins, the Cubs' flame-throwing righty. Like most pitchers, Jenkins tried to get Roberto to chase bad pitches outside. This one was not bad enough. Roberto reached out and slammed it into the stands, right near where I was sitting in right field. I almost caught it, but it bounced away and some kid got that souvenir.

If I had known what was riding on that hit, I might have tried harder to get that ball. It put the Pirates ahead 4–0, but we expected that from Roberto. Also, it was his 23rd home run, tying his career best. Also, it gave him 101 runs batted in. He'd never reached the hundred-RBI mark before. Also, it was his 2000th career hit, a milestone that few major leaguers ever achieve. Man, I wish I'd grabbed that ball!

It was a three-way race until the final week of the season, but the Dodgers edged out the Giants by a game and a half, with the Pirates three back.

The Dodgers went on to get swept by the Baltimore Orioles in a not very memorable World Series. All attention turned to the MVP award. There were a lot of great players in the National League that year, but it really came down to

Roberto's bat versus Sandy's arm. Koufax had won an incredible 27 games that year. He had a jaw-dropping ERA of 1.73, and had led his team to the World Series. And he had done it all playing in pain. The arthritis was so bad that 1966 would be Koufax's final year.

Sandy had become a legend for his ability to play through pain. That made Roberto grind his teeth. You see, Roberto himself had had back pains throughout his whole career. He'd suffered many injuries from playing the game as hard as he did. And yet, when he spoke about his injuries or took himself out of the lineup, sportswriters and even his own managers said he was being a baby. But the white pitcher was everybody's hero for playing through his injuries. It was the sportswriters who voted for the MVP. There was, no doubt, still a lot of racism among them. After his bitter experience with the 1960 voting, Roberto had little doubt that Koufax would win in 1966.

Sometimes life brings you good surprises. The MVP for 1966 was not Sandy Koufax. It was Roberto Clemente. We all knew that it was high time Roberto won the MVP. He was overdue. Roberto refused to show false humility. He felt he had earned it. He told a sportswriter, "It's the highest honor a player can hope for, but I was expecting it."

We all teased him about that. "You were expecting Koufax," we said, poking him in the ribs.

The honors kept coming. *The Sporting News* named him National League "Player of the Year." Back in Pittsburgh, he was given the Dapper Dan Award. This award had been founded way back in 1936, and was given to a Pittsburgh athlete in any sport who made contributions to the city both on and off the field. That one was really big for Roberto. While the fans always loved him in Pittsburgh, the sportswriters had not always been kind. They never understood him well, especially when it came to his injuries. They said he was too touchy, and sometimes downright irritable. The Dapper Dan Award meant he was not just a great athlete, but a great citizen as well.

It was the first time in baseball history that a native Puerto Rican had been named Most Valuable Player. It was the first time any Latino player had won the honor in the National League. In 1965 Cuban-born Zoilo Versalles won the MVP of the American League.

When Roberto came home to the island that winter, he was more of a hero than ever before. It was a joyous Christmas season with little Robertito and Luisito and family and friends. Roberto piled everybody into his Cadillac and drove around the island. At the beaches he collected driftwood. Then they went to *La Finca*, the little farm he owned out near the rainforest we called *El Yunque*. Roberto raised pigs, horses, and goats and cultivated fields of coffee and plantain. He had built the farmhouse with his own hands, using bamboo for the interior.

Wherever he went on the island, he was stopped by children and adults. He always spent time with them. He never walked away or cut someone off. I noticed something different in him after that year. Winning the MVP and those other awards took a load off his heart. He had always been so aware of the racism inside and outside of baseball. At last, he was being recognized for the great player he was, regardless of race.

Could it be that our country was overcoming racism? Progress would not come easily. In the next few years, the United States would erupt in a painful battle over civil rights, with riots in the streets of many American cities.

Roberto had another great year in 1967, winning his fourth National League batting title with a glittering .357 average, the best of his career. He didn't get enough help from his teammates, though. The Pirates finished at .500, with an 81–81 record and a disappointing 6th place finish.

One thing happened that season that really made him mad. He told me about it that winter back in Puerto Rico. A man showed up and asked Roberto to take a small part in a movie. They told him it was a benefit for children, and that's why they could pay him only a token $100 for his appearance. Roberto was always ready to help children. He said "Yes, sure."

They were going to shoot the scene at a fan-filled Shea Stadium before a game with the Mets. It wasn't until then that Roberto learned he had been lied to. The film had nothing to do with children. It was a major motion picture, a comedy with Jack Lemmon and Walter Matthau, *The Odd Couple*. In his scene, the script called for Roberto to hit into a triple play. That was it. Roberto walked off the field, mad as a hornet. They got somebody else to fill the role.

He was still mad when the game began, but when he told me about it a week later, he was laughing. "I took a pitch, and I hit it 440 feet over the fence," Roberto said. "I knew where that movie producer was sitting. As I went by I yelled to him, 'Take a picture of *that* for your stinking movie!'"

For the 1968 season, Roberto got a $100,000 contract. He was the Pirates' best player, and they were rewarding him. When *SPORT* magazine asked who were the very best major leaguers, the highest vote-getters were Hank Aaron, Bill Freehan, Bob Gibson, Ron Santo, Carl Yastrzemski and Roberto Clemente. Then Clemente was voted the best of the best.

It turned out to be a terrible year. First, Roberto injured himself. He took a fall that was more serious than anything since the car accident that messed him up at the beginning of his career. Roberto was always a handyman around the house. His house sat way up on top of a high hill overlooking the ocean. It was a beautiful spot, but it could be treacherous. He had a patio on two levels. He was climbing from one level to the other, holding onto an iron railing. Suddenly, the railing pulled out of the wall, and Roberto was falling backwards. The heavy iron bar almost crushed his chest. Clemente got out of the way, but he fell off the edge of the patio, and rolled head over heels more than a hundred feet down the hill. He landed on the back of his neck. He was almost killed. His right shoulder was bruised, and when he saw the doctor he was ordered to wear a brace. He refused to wear the brace.

Roberto Clemente struggled to Florida for spring training in great pain. Then, just as the season was about to start, something terrible happened that overshadowed his pains. The civil rights leader Martin Luther King, Jr. was assassinated. American cities erupted in riots, as the anger of black America boiled over.

Baseball suddenly did not seem so important, even to Roberto Clemente. As a fighter for victims of racism, Dr. King was greatly admired by Clemente. The great civil rights leader had even been a guest at Roberto's house in Puerto Rico, where the two of them discussed the problems of race in America.

Roberto remembered when he had taken his wife, Vera, furniture shopping in New York

City. He had wanted to see one of the beautiful couches in the showroom window. The salesman ushered them off to a different part of the store. This was where they kept the cheaper, inferior furniture, the kind that Puerto Ricans could afford. Roberto was outraged. He pulled out a big wad of cash, and asked if they thought he could afford the good stuff. By that time one of the store managers had recognized him, and tried to smooth things over, offering him a personal tour of all the best furniture. It was too late. Roberto and Vera marched out of that store.

Even for a baseball superstar, racism was still present. How much worse must it be for the poor people? Martin Luther King, Jr. had been the one to give them a voice, to make their demands for equality heard.

Now he was dead, and the cities were in flame. Roberto took the lead. He talked to the other black players on the team and took their words to the Pittsburgh front office. The Pirates were supposed to open the season with a two-game series in Houston. The Pittsburgh and Houston black players, led by Roberto, said the two games should be canceled. For the Pirates and Astros, the season would not start until after the funeral of Martin Luther King, Jr. in recognition of Dr. King's greatness.

Roberto went on to have a bad season. Well, bad for him anyway. He hit .291, an average a lot of players would love to have. But his RBI production was cut in half, and injuries kept him out of a lot of games. For the first time in eight years, Roberto Clemente was not selected for the All-Star Game.

Two months after King was killed, another American civil rights leader, Robert F. Kennedy, was gunned down. American cities seethed with anger. Halfway around the world, America was stuck in a misguided war in Vietnam. 1968 was just a bad year all around.

Chapter 7

Let me tell you a couple of more stories about our Roberto. This one I heard from a girl who grew up to be a professor of sociology. Her name was Juley. Anyway, when she was in high school in Pittsburgh in 1969, she was an intense fan of Roberto's. That wasn't unusual. There were thousands of them. Roberto started out that year pretty badly—a hangover from 1968—and some fans were even booing him. Roberto did not let it bother him. His honesty kept him level. When he won the MVP, he said, "I deserved it." After one game early in the 1969 season, Roberto said, in a matter-of-fact way, "I deserved to be booed. I stunk out there."

So this girl, Juley, had been in the hospital for awhile. When a family friend came back from watching spring training, he had a treat for her. It was a baseball with this scrawled across it in blue ink: "To Juley, I hope that when you get this you are feeling much better. I hope to see you when I get to Pittsburgh. Love, Roberto."

That sealed it for her. Juley covered the walls of her room with pictures of Roberto. She wrote about him in her diary. She went to games whenever she could. She learned where he lived, and went there to stand on the curb, just hoping to get a glimpse of him. Well, wouldn't you know it. She's standing there, and here comes Roberto, walking out to his car with a laundry basket, just like a real person. She almost fainted, but she gathered herself together and went up to him. With her high school girl's crush she blurted out, "I am more in love with you than any person in the world!"

Roberto took it in stride. He'd been famous for many years now. But he was not closed-off either. He smiled and held up the basket. "I'm going to do some laundry," he said. "Do you want to come along?"

Juley's heart pounded. She was overwhelmed. He was talking to her like a regular person, like a friend! He couldn't really mean it! She wasn't worthy of such kindness! It was just too much for her to handle. All she could do was stammer, "Oh, uh, no. No thanks."

He smiled, put his laundry in his car, and drove away. Juley still remembers how kind, how friendly, and how normal Roberto Clemente was. She still smiles and shakes her head at that stammering girl on the curb.

That's the kind of man Roberto was.

Here's another one. That same year, the Pirates were in San Diego to play the Padres. Roberto saw Willie Stargell coming back to the team motel with a big box of fried chicken. It smelled wonderful.

"Hey, Willie, where'd you get that?" Roberto called out.

Stargell smiled and pointed across the wide busy street and down the block, toward a restaurant. Roberto walked over there and got himself a box. He could hardly wait to get back to the motel and dig in. He was walking along the street with his chicken, when a car swerved off the road, nearly hitting him. Four men jumped out of the car. They grabbed him.

Before he could say anything, they threw him into the back seat. One had a gun in his mouth, and another had a knife at this back. Roberto was scared to death, as anyone would be. They drove him up into the hills, away from any people. They stopped the car and made him take off his clothes. They took his wallet and divided up his money. They took his clothes too, leaving him with just his pants. But he did hear that they were speaking Spanish. Before they left, he thought he would take a chance.

"I am Roberto Clemente," he said.

That stopped them in their tracks. He warned

them that since he was famous, the police and the FBI would track them down.

"Naw, you're not *Roberto Clemente*," one of the robbers said.

"Look at my license," he insisted. "And look at this."

He held up his hand. On his finger was a glittering All-Star Game ring with his named carved into it.

"Es verdad!" It's true!

Roberto had no idea of the magic of being Roberto Clemente—of what he meant to the entire Hispanic-American world.

"Here's your clothes back," they said. "Here's your money, and your wallet."

The kidnappers who might have killed him were now almost ready to ask for autographs. They brushed him off, told him to put his tie back on so it looked like nothing happened, and drove him back down to where they'd grabbed him.

And so Roberto found himself walking down the road toward his motel, his head spinning. Suddenly he heard the screech of tires. He turned around, and there they were again! What was going on? Was setting him free a joke? Were they going to kill him now? The car drew up alongside him. Out of the window came arms holding a box.

"You forgot your chicken, man."

A bewildered Roberto took the box of chicken and watched the car roar off down the road.

He just shook his head. His teammates back at the motel were never going to believe this one!

Those people who booed Roberto early in the 1969 season, the ones that thought maybe he was all washed up? They didn't know very much. As the season went on and he felt healthier, his bat came roaring back to life. 1969 will always be remembered as the year of the Miracle Mets. You have to take your hat off to that New York team. It seemed like they had lost a million games since they joined the National League in 1962, and here they were, out of nowhere, knocking off the Orioles in the World Series.

Yeah, the Mets were the toast of baseball that year, but the Pirates were on the prowl. Behind Roberto's once-again golden batting average of .345, they ended the season 14 games over .500, good for third place in the National League East. Roberto was back on the All-Star team.

The year 1970 was supposed to start with a brand-new stadium for the Pirates. Tired old Forbes Field, with too much room in the outfield and too few seats in the stands, was being replaced. The new field was right down where the rivers met in the heart of the city, and it was called Three Rivers Stadium. It was a big, multi-purpose concrete bowl, built so it could play host both to the Pirates and to the Steelers of the National Football League. Those stadiums were all the rage. Busch Stadium started the trend in St. Louis. Now they were all over the league.

Roberto had mixed feelings. Right field at Forbes had become his personal domain. Some people called it the place where triples went to die. But he was excited, like everyone else, to have a brand-new, state-of-the-art ballpark. And he wouldn't miss the rats. He surely would not miss *them*.

Construction was lagging behind schedule, though, and the Pirates started out their season back at good old Forbes Field. They were supposed to move to Three Rivers in mid-May, but the lighting wasn't installed yet. On July 14, Roberto played in yet another All-Star Game, and drove in the tying run in the bottom of the ninth to send the game to extra innings. The National League finally won in the 12th when Pete Rose charged full throttle over the American League catcher in a close play at the plate.

Two days later the Pirates finally opened their new stadium. The fans were not that excited by the new digs, and the Pirates had shockingly low attendance for their first few home games. That all changed on July 24, when the stadium was filled to capacity. That's because July 24 was Roberto Clemente Night.

For at least one night in Pittsburgh, Roberto would get to play in front of hundreds of cheering Puerto Ricans. They had come in by the planeload from San Juan for the big event. For the first time in his life, Melchor Clemente had been coaxed onto an airplane. He was there, along with Luisa. Vera was there too, of course, along with Roberto's three young sons. The festivities started an hour before the game. All the speeches and announcements were made both in Spanish and in English. The Latin players on the team came out, and each one gave Roberto a hug. The crowd went wild.

When Roberto stepped up to the microphone, at first he couldn't speak. He was so overcome by the show of love. Then he pulled himself together and gave a remarkable talk in his soft, beautiful voice. He was speaking both to the crowd in the stadium and to the TV and radio audience back in Puerto Rico.

"I would like to dedicate this honor to all the Puerto Rican mothers. I don't have words to express this thankfulness. I only ask those who are watching this program and are close to their parents, ask for their blessing, and that they have each other. As those friends who are watching this program or listening to it on the radio shake each other's hands as a sign of friendship that unites all of us Puerto Ricans."

He went on to say that he had achieved his triumphs on behalf of all Latino athletes everywhere. He thanked his parents, his family members, and all his friends in Puerto Rico and everywhere.

During the tribute, Roberto received over one hundred trophies and gifts, including a television set, a new car, and, from Pirates owners John Galbreath and Tom Johnson, a trust fund for the college education of the three Clemente boys. $5500 was raised for Children's Hospital to benefit crippled children whose parents could not afford their therapy. There were many gifts and awards, but Roberto had asked in advance for people not to spend money on him, but instead to donate to Children's Hospital. A group of children from that hospital were invited onto the field to accept the check. Among them was Juley, the girl who was too shy to share Roberto's laundry chores. Only now she was in a full body cast, having recently had an operation on her back.

All it took then was announcer Bob Prince to yell, "*Arriba! Arriba!*" The thunderous ovation shook the brand-new stadium. Roberto tipped his cap to the stands. Then he went out and did what he did best, thrilling the fans by rapping out two hits and making two sensational sliding catches.

Yet again, Roberto had great numbers, including a sparkling .352 batting average. And this year brought something the Pirates fans had not seen in awhile, a first-place finish in the NL East. They were swept out of the pennant series by the Cincinnati Reds, but baseball fever was back in the air in Pittsburgh. Roberto was unstoppable, Stargell hid 31 homers, and something special was in the air. 1971 would prove to be another year of destiny.

Chapter 8

If Roberto had decided to retire after the 1970 season, he would still have been considered one of the greatest players ever to play the game. But even though he had to battle through more pains and injuries, the passion for baseball still burned white-hot in him. He had not tasted the excitement of a World Series for a full decade, since the magical 1960 season.

The 1971 Pirates had a lot of young players who joked around and always kept the clubhouse upbeat. The team looked very much different than the last Pirates team in the world series. Back then, Roberto was practically the only dark-skinned player on the team. But the Pirates had been very aggressive in acquiring black and Latino players, and now most of the team was non-white. On September 1, in a historic moment, the Pittsburgh Pirates would be the first major league baseball team ever to field an entire team of players who were black.

It was truly an important event, but the team tried not to make a big deal out of it. When a reporter asked the manager, Danny Murtaugh, about it after the game, Murtaugh pretended not to have noticed. "Did I have nine blacks out there?" he said. "I thought I had nine Pirates out there. Once a man puts on a Pirate uniform, I don't notice the color of his skin."

The players did notice, though. Roberto told me that both the white and black players were laughing and teasing each other about it. That was the kind of loose and fun team they had that year.

Of all the feisty guys on that team, one of the funniest and most outspoken was a young pitcher named Dock Ellis. He was full of practical jokes, and was pitching lights-out too, well enough to be named the starter in the All-Star Game. One time Ellis brought Muhammad Ali into the locker room. He teased the great boxer, saying, "I'm prettier than you are," and doing an imitation of the Ali shuffle. Ali just laughed.

On another day, Ellis was standing in front of his locker grooving to the music, which was turned up loud. When Roberto came in the room, somebody turned the music down. Ellis couldn't resist. "Did you notice how the room went silent when the great one enters?" he asked, bowing toward Roberto. Then Ellis did his Roberto imitation, twitching his neck back and forth the way Roberto did as he came up to bat, and speaking in a fake Latino accent, "I not like I used to be. I a little bit of an old man."

A few years earlier, nobody would have dared to pull something like that around Roberto. But Roberto had mellowed. He was assured of his place on this team, and in baseball history. He laughed with the rest of the team at Dock's antics.

Roberto's bat had not mellowed, though. His team tore up the National League East, and Roberto went to yet another All-Star Game, this time in Detroit, home of the American League Tigers. This All-Star Game became famous for its home runs.

I was lucky enough to be there for that historic game. Like everyone else, I could not believe the homer hit by young slugger Reggie Jackson. With two strikes on him, Jackson smashed a ball that people still say today was the longest home run ever hit in baseball. My head snapped up to follow it. It seemed to be still going up as it left the field. If it hadn't crashed into a transformer high up on the light tower in right center field, I swear that ball might have made it into orbit.

In the bottom of the eighth inning, Roberto came up to bat. Besides Reggie Jackson, four other future Hall-of-Famers had already hit home runs. Catcher Johnny Bench, who would lead the Big Red Machine dynasty in Cincinnati, got the first one. Then came Hank Aaron, future home run king, ripping one out of the park. Then came Reggie's blast. Then the Orioles great Frank Robinson knocked one out, and Twins powerful first baseman Harmon Killebrew lofted one deep into the upper deck in left field.

Roberto was never a big home-run hitter. He hit for average, and used his speed to make doubles and triples out of singles. I swear I saw a gleam in his eye as he dug in at the plate that day. He knew the reputation of the men who had homered before him. He knew he belonged among the best of the best.

Hometown hero Mickey Lolich was pitching. They loved him in Detroit, and he did not want to let them down. So he didn't want to mess around with Roberto at all. Like so many pitchers before him, he refused to give Roberto anything good to hit. After the first two pitches, both way outside, Roberto stepped out and flipped his bat in the air. I could tell he was not happy. Still, Lolich would not give in, and the count went to 3–1. Roberto stared out fiercely, as if to say, "Give me something, anything." Lolich gave him nothing. Ball four was way high and outside. Roberto didn't care. Roberto's bat was so quick. He reached across and took that high fastball right out of the park.

The National League championship series opened in San Francisco. The Pirates were sobered by the knowledge that they had lost five straight games here during the regular season. Roberto never liked playing in the swirling winds of Candlestick Park. The Giants had superstars Willie Mays and Willie McCovey in the field, and top-flight pitchers Juan Marichal and Gaylord Perry at the top of the rotation. In the first game, the Pirates got two early unearned runs on Giant miscues, but it wasn't enough. The Giants came back to win 5–4, and the Pirates looked nervous. Roberto became the cheerleader. "We'll win this," he declared with an optimistic smile, "and the World Series."

The Pirates came back and won the second game, breaking the Candlestick curse. They returned to Three Rivers Stadium tied, and did not lose again to the Giants, taking the series 3–1. There were some worrisome signs, though. In an unusual slump, Pirates slugger Willie Stargell went 0–14 in the series, and failed to drive in any runs. Roberto stepped it up, hitting .333 and driving in four runs. He wasn't satisfied with himself, though. He said his back was hurting and he wasn't swinging well.

Nobody really thought it mattered anyway. The Pirates now had to face the defending world champion Baltimore club. The Orioles had ended the regular season on an 11-game win streak, and their pitching staff had, incredibly, *four* 20-game winners. Just like eleven years ago, the Pirates entered the World Series as underdogs to a powerful American League club. The Las Vegas oddsmakers set up Baltimore as the favorites.

The night before Game 1, Roberto invited me to have a quiet dinner at a restaurant with Vera and him. I had a steak, and I tried to get Roberto to join me. I teased him, saying red meat would make him strong. He laughed and said we were island people. Seafood makes us strong.

A couple hours later, Roberto wished to heaven that he had taken my advice. That was some bad seafood. He started throwing up, and it got so bad we called for an ambulance. But stubborn Roberto refused go to the hospital.

"Look, man," I pleaded with him, "this is bad. You need help."

"No," he said. "They will say, 'That Roberto Clemente, he's playing sick again.'"

Even though he was badly dehydrated, there was no convincing him. Finally we got the medics to hook up an IV to him in his hotel bed.

Roberto made us promise not to tell anyone. Against medical advice, he ran out there for Game 1. He played well, but the rest of the team looked sick, and the Pirates lost 5–3.

Game 2 got postponed a day because of rain. When they did play, the Orioles reeled off an impressive 11–0 win. The sportswriters were saying how overmatched the pitiful Pirates were. The great Orioles outfielder Frank Robinson knew better. When a writer asked him if the game was "a laugher," Robinson set him straight. "No. We'll laugh after we've won four games."

Roberto was not happy. Even though he had been the Pirates' best player, with four hits in the first two games, he wasn't happy with his game, and he was disgusted by the playing field in Baltimore. He had thought Candlestick Park was bad. He'd never played before on the mudflats of Memorial Stadium. The professional football team had just played on the same field, and the grass was all torn up. "This is not a major league ballpark," Roberto said to the media. "You have to worry about holes. You can't get to the ball."

He was glad to be going back to Pittsburgh for Game 3.

Back in his first World Series eleven years earlier, Roberto's biggest play might have been when he beat out a scratch single against the Yankees to keep the Pirates alive. Something similar happened in Game 3 of this World Series.

The Pirates were nursing a slim 2–1 lead in the seventh inning when Roberto came up. On a bad pitch, Roberto started to swing but held up. His bat accidentally clipped the ball and sent it rolling back toward the pitcher. It should have been an easy out, but the pitcher was well aware of Roberto's speed. He scrambled off the mound and got the ball in a hurry, but rushed his throw. It went wide, pulling the first baseman off the bag.

That small advantage led to a three-run inning and a win for Pittsburgh.

Getting ready for Game 4 was a challenge. It would be the first night game ever played in a World Series. The executives at NBC-TV decided they could make a lot more money if they put the game on at night. Millions more fans would be able to see the event. Millions would be seeing the amazing Roberto Clemente.

The Pirates won that night game behind the three-for-four hitting of Roberto, and then went back to Baltimore and won again. Roberto was nothing short of awesome. His teammate, star pitcher Steve Blass, did not mince words, "The rest of us were just players. Clemente was a prince." Sportswriter Jim Murray, who had ridiculed the Pirates earlier, now wrote, "The greatest player this town will ever see came not out of the crucibles or the mine shafts or the ore boats, but out of the canebreaks of the Caribbean."

The Pirates needed just one more win to clinch the series. As they ran out on the field for Game 6, the prize was so close they could smell it, taste it. The Pirates jumped to a 2–0 lead when Roberto smashed a home run in the second Baltimore fought back to a tie, and the game went into extra innings. If not for Roberto's arm,

Baltimore might have won in the bottom of the ninth. With two out and one on, an Oriole lashed a double down the line in Roberto's direction. If that ball had been hit at an ordinary right-fielder, it might easily have scored the run. Roberto was anything but ordinary. He shut the mouths of the cheering Baltimore fans with a huge throw to the catcher that sent the base runner scrambling back to third.

In the top of the tenth, Roberto could have won the game—if the Orioles had given him a chance. With two outs and a runner in scoring position, the Baltimore manager was not about to take a chance. Roberto had already clubbed a triple and a home run in the game. What they gave Roberto now was an intentional walk, with the catcher standing so far out to the side that even Roberto had no chance to swing. It turned out to be a wise move. The Orioles got out of the inning, and went on to win in the bottom of the tenth.

The series was now tied 3–3. There would be a Game 7 for all the marbles. What had seemed like victory day had turned to white-knuckle time.

Roberto took up his role as head cheerleader again, rousing his troops, raising their flagging spirits. "Don't worry," he said, "we are gonna win this game. No problem." Privately, though, he was thinking ahead. His back was hurting again. Vera told me he said before the game that if the Pirates won, he would retire from baseball. She couldn't believe it. Baseball was his passion, his life.

The Memorial Stadium fans roared as Game 7 got underway. It was a dreary day, with dark clouds off in the distance. It was so dark that afternoon that they turned on the stadium lights. The hometown Orioles looked as if they were taking care of business. Pitcher Mike Cuellar waltzed through the first three innings. Meanwhile, the Pirates' Steve Blass was laboring deep into counts and getting in trouble in every inning. It looked like only a matter of time before Baltimore broke through.

Cuellar continued his dominance in the fourth, getting two quick outs. Then Roberto came to bat. Our Roberto, turning his neck from side to side to get the kinks out, strolled to the plate like a man on a leisurely golf outing. That was when Cuellar made a mistake. He hung a curve ball out over the plate, and Roberto slammed it 390 feet over the left field wall. The Pirates had a 1–0 lead.

It was kind of funny it happened that way. You see, Roberto had been Cuellar's manager a year earlier in winter ball. When Cuellar faced the powerful Reggie Jackson, Roberto told his pitcher to pitch inside so Jackson couldn't get a big swing. Cuellar didn't listen, and hung a ball that Jackson promptly hit out of the park. Cuellar thought Roberto was too overbearing and quit the team. And here he was in Game 7 of the World Series making the same mistake with Roberto he had made with Reggie Jackson.

Pirate pitcher Steve Blass was so nervous he could barely stand. Earlier in the year, when Blass had made an error that cost the Pirates a game, a despondent Blass kept muttering, "I'm nothing!" It was Roberto Clemente who came to him and lifted his spirits and made him believe in himself again.

Now Blass tried to believe in himself again. The Pirates scored another run in the eighth, but the Orioles answered with a run of their own. At the top of the ninth, Blass was tired, but the manager was showing faith in him. No reliever was called in to finish the game. It was all up to Blass, and he had to pitch aggressively. He could not make a mistake now. He faced Baltimore's best hitters, Boog Powell and Frank Robinson, and got them out easily. Merv Rettenmund hit the ball straight up the middle, usually a hit. But the Pirates had done their homework, and shortstop Jackie Hernandez was in the right place. He stopped the ball at the outfield grass. He fired the ball to first for the final out. The Pittsburgh Pirates were the world champions again.

That ending served the Baltimore manager Earl Weaver right. Earlier that season he told reporters that the Pirates could never win with Hernandez at shortstop. Hernandez was a loser, he said. Now Earl Weaver was the loser.

Hernandez made the last out, and Blass pitched a gutsy game, but Roberto was the star. He was named World Series MVP, an obvious choice. He had 12 hits in 29 at bats, a .414 batting average. He hit two home runs and had four RBIs. He'd shown great base running, and had uncorked some amazing throws from right field. In the clubhouse, reporters mobbed around him for more than an hour. Roberto spoke first in Spanish. "On this the proudest day of my life," he said, addressing his parents, "I ask for your blessing." That he had chosen to speak first in Spanish touched the hearts of millions of Latinos watching on television.

Baseball fans had always known Roberto was great, but Pittsburgh was not a major market. He was not nearly so famous as he should have been. In the 1971 World Series, Roberto had a stage big enough for his talent, and the entire nation now knew he was one of the very best ever to play the game.

Roberto was a loyal teammate, and he knew he had not done it alone. In all the wildness after the game, he had not had a chance to congratulate Steve Blass on his gutsy complete-game win. Blass would never forget what happened on the charter plane back to Pittsburgh. It was one of the most meaningful moments of his life. Roberto Clemente came back to where he was sitting and said, "Blass, come out here. Let me embrace you."

Because of the 1971 World Series, Roberto Clemente became nationally famous. Roberto was now accepted as a truly great player.

Chapter 9

W̲hat about Roberto's threat to retire if the Pirates won the World Series?

Well, that had a lot to do with Vera. In the joyful moments of the Game 7 celebration, Roberto ran from the field to embrace his wife. She was crying like a river, like a flood. The first words out of her mouth were, "Don't quit now, Roberto, please! Baseball is your life!" Amid all the cheering and screaming and hugging around him, he stopped, looked deep into her eyes, and knew she meant it. What could he say to that? She was the mother of his beloved sons, and the one who had to sacrifice the most through the long season when her husband spent so much time on the road. Roberto was back in baseball! In fact, he never left. No one knew how close he had come to retiring.

Roberto traveled to New York to accept the MVP award from *SPORT* magazine. The prize was a hot car, a Dodge Charger, but it became apparent that Roberto had more important things on his mind. He had always been a confident man on and off the field, but now he spoke with a new authority. He stood tall in his perfectly tailored suit and spoke his mind. People listened.

One thing he said was that it was high time major league baseball had its first black manager. He didn't put himself forward for the high honor, but instead spoke about people like Ernie Banks and Frank Robinson. That showed what kind of man Roberto was. During the series, he and Robinson had thrown some barbs at each other through the media. But that was all behind him now. Roberto knew what kind of man Robinson was, too. Sure enough, Robinson would go on to become, a few years later, the first black manager in the major leagues.

Roberto also expressed support for the players who were trying to get more say in where they played and how much money they were able to make. He remembered how helpless it felt to be hidden away in Montreal, not even allowed to play, at the start of his career.

But the subject that really got him going was his dream to build a Sports City for the young people of Puerto Rico. He knew there were problems with drugs and crime holding back many kids, and he was passionate to do something about it. He said he didn't care about winning things for himself, but it meant he could do more to help others. Through baseball he would make Puerto Rico and America a better place. He said he wanted to "show all the kids how to live and how to play with other kids." His voice swelled with emotion as he spoke. He went on, "I get kids together and talk about the importance of sports, the importance of being a good citizen, the importance of respecting their mother and father. I like to get together with the fathers and the sons and talk to them. Then we go to the ball field, and I show them some techniques of playing baseball."

I wish you could have been there. You could never know how sincere and moving Roberto could be unless you heard him for yourself. He believed in family, country, and baseball, and he wanted to build a Sports City to inspire those values in young people.

At Sports City, children would receive practical instruction in baseball, swimming, tennis, and other recreational sports as well as tutoring in academic subjects. He wanted more Puerto Rican youth to learn the values of teamwork and personal sacrifice. Roberto himself was blessed to have a strong and loving family with strong values, but he knew that many youngsters now came from broken and troubled homes. The streets held terrible temptations, including drugs and gangs.

Roberto estimated his Sports City would cost about $2.5 million. He visited the governor of Puerto Rico to ask for federal money for the project. The governor was interested and sympathetic, and Roberto was optimistic that the money would be there. Roberto took his family to his beloved *La Finca*, his farm. Hundreds of people thronged around him. They rang his doorbell day and night. Strangers hailed him as *El Magnifico*. Every civic club wanted to host a banquet for Roberto. It was too much. He was so stressed he lost ten pounds. They were smothering him with love and admiration.

The Clementes took a long vacation throughout South America, visiting Caracas, Venezuela; Rio de Janeiro and Sao Paulo, Brazil; Lima, Peru; and Santiago, Chile, among other places. Everywhere he went he was greeted as a hero who had brought respect to the Spanish-speaking world. The trip had to be cut short when Roberto's father took sick.

Roberto hurried home to Puerto Rico. He visited his father in the hospital and was glad to learn he was not seriously ill. However, the patient in the next bed was in agony with terrible back pain. While Vera Clemente guarded the door to make sure no doctors or nurses came in, Roberto began massaging the man. The next day, when Roberto visited his father, the other man was getting ready to leave the hospital. He tearfully thanked Roberto for his miraculous touch. It was not the first time his hands had healed another person. Roberto had a gift. He bought a small house near his home, and planned to open aa small chiropractic clinic there so he and others could help people. Roberto believed in alternative medicines because he had seen results in himself and others.

Word that Roberto Clemente had healing powers in his hands spread in the neighborhood, and people with aches and pains would appear at his door. He would not turn them away. He did his best to massage away their pain and had a great deal of success.

As the 1972 spring training season loomed, Roberto had his usual host of aches and pains, plus some that were new. He had two rheumatic heels, tendinitis in his ankles, inflammation of both Achilles tendons, and repeated viral infections. His weight kept dropping. In spite of this, he drank his famous milkshakes and was determined to be a valuable Pittsburgh Pirate.

Roberto began his 18th season with the Pirates. It was supposed to open April 5, but the players voted to strike for better health and pension benefits. It was the first strike in major league baseball history. Though he was uncomfortable with the idea, Roberto supported the players' goals. The strike ended with a player victory, and the season finally started on April 15.

Once more Roberto played with intensity and pride. In a June 19 game against the Dodgers, he got a two-run home run in the eighth inning to top a three-RBI night and lead the Pirates to a victory over the Dodgers. The three RBIs gave Roberto a career total of 1,275 RBIs, the most of any player in Pirate history.

It was a tough season for Roberto. He was thirty-eight, a senior citizen of the game. With all his aches and injuries, he played in only 102 games that season, the fewest of his career. He hit .312, which is a dream average for many players, but was a bit disappointing to Roberto.

The defending World Series champs were playing well as a team. They were loose and confident, teasing each other endlessly in the clubhouse. Roberto gave out and received his share of ribbing with the rest. Roberto always put team success ahead of personal statistics, but there was one huge milestone looming that neither he nor the team nor the media could ignore. Coming into the season, Roberto needed 118 hits to have 3,000 in his career. That's something only ten players in the history of the game had accomplished.

His friends Willie Mays and Hank Aaron had already joined the very exclusive club that also included such legends as Ty Cobb, Stan Musial and Honus Wagner. But with all the injuries, it looked doubtful for Roberto. Then, just when everyone was ready to wait until next year, Roberto went on a late-season hitting tear. He banged out four hits against St. Louis, added another three against the Mets, got one more against Montreal. Suddenly the record was within striking distance, just six hits away. People all over the country were watching. The last road trip of the year was to Philadelphia. Roberto went in there and clubbed five hits in three games. He was so hot his manager had the confidence to pull him from the game so he could get the record before the home fans in Pittsburgh.

On September 29, Roberto went for number 3,000. The Pirates were playing the New York Mets. It was Roberto against future Hall-of-Famer Tom Seaver. Roberto walked to the plate, giving a nod to the already cheering fans, who expected to see a historic moment unfold. In his career, some of Roberto's biggest hits had been little dribblers that he beat out with his amazing speed. Now it happened again. Roberto hit a weak grounder up the middle and sprinted to first. In his hurry to get Roberto, the second baseman had the ball glance off his glove. The scoreboard lit up with a big H for hit. The Pittsburgh fans went crazy, screaming and cheering their hero. Streamers were unfurled.

But the joyous moment was short-lived. Cries of joy turned to gasps and then boos. The magic H disappeared to be replaced by an E. The scorekeeper ruled it was not a hit after all, but an error on the second baseman. Amid grumbling fans and a disappointed Roberto, the game ended.

After the game, Roberto was furious. All of the slights and prejudices from his long career came roaring into his mind. He'd been robbed. "I know it was a hit," Roberto fumed. "Everybody knew it was a hit." All the old resentments boiled over. But then Roberto learned the name of the scorekeeper. It was Luke Quay, a man whose judgment Roberto trusted completely. Roberto stopped complaining about the call and made no more claims of racism. After the press had left, Roberto got a baseball and wrote something on it: *"It was a hit. No, it was an error. No, it was superman Luke Quay. To my friend Luke with best wishes, Roberto Clemente."* He had the ball sent over to Quay. That was his way of apologizing. That's the kind of man Roberto was.

On the morning of September 30, Three Rivers Stadium had a smaller crowd than usual. It was a cloudy day, a fall Saturday when football-crazy Pittsburgh turned its attention to college gridiron games. But the fans who did come cheered lustily when their hero appeared. The game was being broadcast in Spanish to Puerto Rico. Just about every radio on the island was turned on.

The first time Roberto stepped up to the plate, he struck out. There were murmurs of disappointment in the stands. But he knew he'd get another chance. He came up to the plate a second time. All eyes were on him. Roberto twisted his neck back and forth and took his usual stance, away from the plate, legs wide apart. The bat in Roberto's hands cracked, and he banged a double off the wall. As he stood calmly on second base and the crowd cheered, there was no doubt. Roberto Clemente was a career 3,000-hit man.

As he strolled out to right field in the next inning, the crowd was still roaring. Roberto took off his cap, raising it into the air. One famous picture of the moment shows Clemente's back, with his number 21 emblazoned on the back of his uniform. Later, when questioned on his low-key response to the great moment, Clemente said, "I never was a big shot, and I never will be a big shot."

Before the season ended, one more record fell to Roberto. He passed Honus Wagner for the most games ever played by one man in a Pittsburgh Pirate uniform, 2,433.

Let me tell you one more story about the kind of hitter Roberto Clemente was. This one was told to me by Fernando Gonzalez, our countryman who had just made it to the majors. He adored Roberto, and watched his every move, the way Roberto had once watched Monte Irvin's every move. That fall, as Roberto was ripping toward his 3,000 hits, there was this game against Chicago. The Cubs had Ferguson Jenkins on the mound. Fergie was at the top of his game. He'd won the Cy Young Award the year before and was about to finish his 6th straight 20-win season. It was the best against the best. The first time Roberto came up to bat, he took a strike on the low inside corner. Roberto was never known to watch too many pitches go by. Later, back in the dugout, Gonzalez asked him about it, saying "I know you can hit that pitch."

"Just keep watching," Roberto said calmly, "and you'll see why I took that pitch."

In the seventh inning, there was a man on base, and the game was on the line. Roberto came to the plate and stood in against Jenkins. At a crucial moment in the count, Jenkins came in low and tight—the exact same pitch that seemed to have frozen Roberto in the first inning. This time Roberto whacked it into the seats in right center field. After trotting around the bases, Roberto stepped into the dugout, and his eyes met those of young Gonzalez. "That," Roberto said, "is why I gave him that pitch in the first inning."

Fernando could only shake his head in amazement. Roberto could do things like that, and he did them routinely. And he did them against some of the best pitchers baseball has ever seen: Jenkins, Seaver, Bob Gibson, Don Sutton.

The list goes on.

Eventually, some managers around the league just gave up trying to get him out. They called it "The Clemente Rule," and it went something like this: Don't try to bait him by pitching outside, because he kills outside pitches. Don't try to intimidate him by pitching inside, because that will make him mad, and he'll hit a home run. Just throw it down the middle and let him get his hits.

The Pirates cruised to first place in the National League East. They were a great team. But Roberto was tired, and there was another great team in the National League. The Cincinnati Reds were gearing up a dynasty of their own, with Johnny Bench, Tony Perez, Joe Morgan and Pete Rose leading the Big Red Machine. The exciting five-game series went the distance, but when the dust settled, the Reds had prevailed in the final game, 4–3. The winning run scored on a wild pitch by Pirate pitcher Bob Moose. After the game, the Pirates were disappointed, and Moose was crushed. He sat all alone in a corner of the locker room, shaking his head and cursing himself. It was Roberto who came over and sat next to him. It was Roberto who said, "Don't worry about it any more. It's gone."

Chapter 10

In spite of losing the pennant, the season had been a good one for Roberto. He batted .312, got his 3000th hit, and won his 12th Golden Glove. But more and more of his attention was focused away from the game, on helping other people.

He had signed a three-year promotional deal with Eastern Airlines. The main thing he got in return was that the airline would sponsor baseball clinics for poor children in Puerto Rico. There would be a clinic in his own town of Carolina as well as in Ponce and Mayaguez and other places. Until Roberto could realize his big dream of the Sports City for youngsters, this would provide some immediate benefits.

Roberto had a long friendship with the team announcer Bob Prince. Roberto liked the off-beat announcer who had worked up the fans for years by shouting *Arriba!* when Roberto came to bat. At a celebration to mark the announcer's 25th year in broadcasting, Roberto gave a speech and presented Prince an amazing gift, the silver bat Roberto won for his first batting title back in 1961.

Roberto was named manager for the Puerto Rican team at the World Baseball Championships that would take place in November and December 1972. The host city for the games was Managua, Nicaragua. No one knew then how that place would change history for the Clemente family.

Roberto arrived in Nicaragua in late November. He found the people charming, and he mingled with them on the streets. Wherever Roberto went, all over the world, he made friends with the ordinary people. He was drawn to children, especially to sick children. He visited *El Retiro* hospital in Nicaragua and found a young boy in a wheelchair. Roberto knelt beside the wheelchair and asked the boy his story. The boy had been playing on the railroad tracks. A train came so fast he could not escape. One of his legs was severed and the other badly mangled. The boy, Julio Parrales, could not walk. There was no money for him to get a prosthetic device or for therapy to teach him to walk again. He seemed condemned to spend the rest of his life in the wheelchair. Moved with compassion, Roberto started a fund to help the boy. All the players in the championship games pitched in, and soon there was money for the prosthetic.

Roberto told Julio that soon he would be able to walk again and he, Roberto, would help him. He told Julio that in the next baseball tournament in Nicaragua, Julio would be a batboy. Roberto promised to watch for the boy in the dugout. The conversation sent a surge of hope into the boy's heart. Roberto had shown him a future he thought was closed to him.

After the tournament in Nicaragua, Roberto returned to his family in Puerto Rico to prepare for the festive Christmas holidays. But then came the disaster that changed everything.

At around midnight on December 23, a sudden chill blew across Managua, Nicaragua. The animals were restless. They seemed to sense something terrible was coming. Then the earth began to tremble sideways. A second rumble was even stronger, and this time the earth seemed to move up and down. Finally, the third and most violent of the tremors, estimated to be around 6.5 on the Richter scale, seemed to grab Managua and shake it. Three hundred and fifty square blocks of Managua were destroyed. Houses and stores tumbled into masses of debris. Broken pipes spewed water and gas, and fires broke out. People all over the city fled their homes and were milling in terror in the street. Over five thousand people died, and many more thousands were injured. A quarter of a million people lost their homes.

Nicaragua was a poor country to begin with, and its people could not cope with such a massive disaster. The largest country in Central America, Nicaragua had a population of less than four million people. Most were *mestizos*, mixed Spanish and Indians who lived on meager farms. They were barely surviving in the best of times, and many in the large city of Managua lived in shanty towns with few conveniences. Because of rising oil prices and the resultant growing inflation, the people were struggling. Called the "land of lakes and volcanoes," Nicaragua was subject to earthquakes, but this one was devastating in the extreme.

From their home on the hill in *Rio Piedras*, the Clementes heard the terrible news. Coming so soon after Roberto had spent almost a month in Nicaragua and after he had made so many friends, it was more like a family tragedy. These were not strange and distant people. Roberto had walked with them, shaken their hands. He remembered the boy with the mangled legs. What had happened to Julio, and to all the young players in the sports competition?

Roberto was frantic to learn more about the disaster. The radio and television broadcasts were sketchy. Roberto scoured the island, and finally found ham radio operators who were hearing up-to-the-minute reports from Managua. The news

By December 27, it was apparent to the relief agencies that the supplies were disappearing in Managua. Red Cross workers told Roberto that the minute the planes landed with relief supplies, Somoza's soldiers would surround the plane and take everything. Nobody knew where it went. Roberto was outraged. He was working himself and the rest of us into exhaustion, and the supplies were not even getting to the people who needed them. Something had to be done.

I was with Roberto when he heard the story of a brave American medical team. When their plane landed in Managua, they were met by one of Somoza's sons who wanted to know if they had any barbed wire to put around the cargo for safe-keeping. The doctors said no, the supplies were needed right now. After a tense standoff, they loaded their mobile hospital into trucks and moved past the troops to take relief personally to the Nicaraguan people. They had faced down the son of the dictator.

Roberto looked up. His eyes were shining with tears of determination. "People know me," he said. "They know my name. I can make sure the supplies get to the people!"

"Roberto," I said, "are you saying you're going to go to Managua?"

"Yes," he said, and I knew immediately there would be no talking him out of it.

That same day we got an urgent request from was worse than anyone could imagine. There were hundreds or thousands dead. No one knew how many were trapped in the rubble of collapsed houses. There were people, covered with blood, roaming the streets, crying for help.

Roberto forgot all about his own holiday plans. Christmas was the most important time in Puerto Rico, but all this could wait. Roberto said, "I am going to do something about this." He quickly established a special committee in Puerto Rico to collect relief supplies for Nicaragua. This project was all he cared about. A broadcaster, Myron Cope, once said of Roberto, "Clemente was an emotional man and that was his beauty. It drove him not only to physical anguish, but also to nearly incredible performances on the field as well as to the good works he was engaged in."

Many celebrities lend their names to worthy causes to help raise money, but don't get personally involved. Roberto put his heart and soul into this effort. I saw it for myself. He called for able-bodied people to come out to help, and I came. We all worked hard those days, but Roberto worked harder. The way he threw himself into it made me think of the way he played baseball, hurling himself into walls to make the big catches, tearing around the base paths at top speed after a hit.

Roberto went on television in Puerto Rico to ask for relief supplies, food, clothing and medical supplies. He worked fourteen hours a day, refusing to eat or rest. He looked exhausted. I said to him, "Roberto, man, you need to take a rest." He said, "Yeah, sure."

I thought he was going home for awhile. Then I found out he'd headed out to the better neighborhoods of San Juan. He was going door to door, personally asking people for money. Imagine. A knock at the door, and here's Roberto Clemente asking you to help the people of Nicaragua. Who could say no? Roberto quickly raised $150,000 to buy 26 tons of food, clothing and medicine. Some large companies sent donations in by the truckload. Hiram Bithorn Stadium in Santurce became the central collection point where we all worked to get the supplies organized for transport.

I thought the government would take over from there. Surely the United States could send an army transport plane. But Roberto said that would take too long. He knew nothing about international cargo, but that didn't stop him. With a couple of phone calls he leased a Lockheed Constellation, one of those planes called "Super Snoopy." It was supposed to make three trips to Managua. Volunteers loaded the first shipment, including desperately-needed X-ray machines and other medical supplies.

Puerto Rico was not the only place that mobilized to help, of course. All around the United States and the Caribbean, people were also

collecting relief supplies. Church congregations, the Red Cross, and U.S. Army troops were uniting to help, but Puerto Rico, under Roberto's leadership, was one of the first responders.

The Super Snoopy set off for Nicaragua with Roberto watching from the side of the runway, willing the big plane to get there fast. Then he waited for reports from his ham radio contacts that the supplies were getting to the people.

The reports that came back were very disturbing. The supplies were not getting to the people. Nicaragua's military dictator, General Somoza Debayle, was more concerned about keeping order than giving relief to his people. Troops were ordered to shoot looters on sight. On the streets, mutilated bodies lay untended, and the smell of death was overwhelming. Thousands of people were begging for food. Vultures circled overhead, drawn by so much death. There was little relief of any kind reaching the survivors.

Roberto spent the day after Christmas on the parking lot of Bithorn Stadium. People were constantly arriving with food and cash. Roberto shouted into a microphone that all checks had to be made out to the Roberto Clemente Relief Committee for Nicaragua, not to him. Troops of students arrived to help load the supplies. There would soon be enough to fill a second Super Snoopy. Volunteers worked all night to load the plane.

relief workers in Nicaragua. They needed sugar, flour, and medical supplies. Roberto sprang into action. He said we had all those things sitting on the ground right here. He needed another plane to get the supplies there fast. He would lease a bigger plane, and ride along with the crew to make sure the help got to the people.

There was no way for Roberto to know that the DC-7 he leased had such a troubled past. Or that the twenty-six-year-old who owned it, Arthur Rivera, had been cited several times for safety problems. The plane was legally registered with a company whose name sounded good, American Air Express. In truth, that plane was a piece of junk with a new paint job, silvery white with a lightning bolt on the side.

Rivera had taken the DC-7 for a trial run earlier, and as he taxied around the airstrip, he lost steering control, sending the plane careening into a drainage ditch. It had two blown tires, bent propeller blades, and other engine damage. After it was repaired, the FAA inspectors recommended that a new engine be installed, but they did not insist on it. Rivera ignored them.

That plane made us all nervous. Vera didn't like the look of it at all. I could tell that kid Rivera was shady. But there was no talking to Roberto. Instead of backing off, he was trying to get other ballplayers to come with him. His teammate Jose Pagan took one look at the plane and said "no way," and told Roberto he shouldn't go either.

On the day they were heading out, seven-year-old Robertito Clemente pleaded with his father not to go to Managua. The little boy did not like it when his father went on flights. He was so unhappy about it he sometimes tried to hide his plane tickets. Robertito told his grandmother the same thing. His father should not fly to Managua. But nobody took the boy seriously. He was just a small child who loved his father and missed him when he went away.

Afterwards, the things we found out just made us furious. First there was the pilot. Rivera hired a Texan named Jerry Hill. Here's how the job interview went:

Rivera: "Can you fly a DC-7?"

Hill, "Yeah, I love DC-7s."

What Hill did not mention was that he'd just been laid off by another airline. He was facing a hearing for violations in the last fourteen months, and might lose his license.

The captain is supposed to oversee the loading of the aircraft. Hill was sleeping in the cockpit, and the trucks just kept coming with more stuff. That plane was already overloaded, and here came a pick-up truck at the last minute with sixteen bags of sugar that weighed sixty pounds each, plus a bunch of other supplies. The workers, not knowing any better, put it all on the plane, in the only place left, up near the cockpit, throwing off the weight distribution. They didn't even tie the stuff down.

The flight was scheduled to leave at four o'clock in the morning. Mechanical troubles caused delays that lasted all morning and all afternoon. It was not until 5 p.m. that they called Roberto and said they were ready to go. Roberto kissed his wife goodbye and drove to the airport.

Roberto got aboard, but as the DC-7 taxied down the runway, there were more mechanical problems. Back to the hangar again. The delay went on for hours. Finally, at 9:20 p.m., the DC-7 came back to the runway and was given clearance by the tower to take off. Hill was in the pilot's seat, with Rivera as co-pilot beside him. Between them, a little farther back, was Roberto Clemente.

As the plane lumbered down the runway, airport workers who were watching knew it was in trouble. It looked overloaded. The nose was too far down. It was going way too slow. The heavy old plane used all of the runway's 9,000 feet to get off the ground, and then barely cleared the trees.

Immediately the workers heard the gunshot-like sounds of engine backfires. The plane was in deep trouble now. As the engine flamed, the pilot tried to abort the flight and return to the airport. He turned sharply left. There was an explosion. Then more explosions. The DC-7 dove nose-first into the Atlantic Ocean a mile and a half from shore. Within minutes it had vanished.

Seconds after the DC-7 vanished from the radar screen, the U.S. Coast Guard Rescue Center was alerted. Teams rushed to the beachfront scene, beaming lights on the water.

At 12:30 a.m., Vera Clemente got a phone call from her niece. The young woman was crying. She said something about a plane crash. Vera didn't understand. Her husband had left hours and hours ago for the airport. He must be in Managua by now. There had to be some mistake.

By dawn, the shoreline was teeming with people. Three helicopters and a pair of fixed-wing aircraft as well as two smaller vessels and the cutter *Sagebrush* searched the water. The Atlantic was rough. Some debris, but not bodies, had surfaced. Seat cushions floated in the waves. An oil slick grew on the water.

Vera Clemente came to a roped-off area called Pinones Beach, the nearest point to where her husband and the others had vanished. Six U.S. divers went into the water. Roberto's good friend, Pirate catcher Manny Sanguillen, went into the water too, searching for his friend.

The water was about 150 feet deep where the DC-7 dropped. More pieces of debris appeared atop the turbulent, dark waves. A grapefruit, life jackets, luggage, one shoe, a pair of new gray slacks, boxes with relief supplies inside. Some of the debris was charred from the fire. A large part of the plane was found about a mile and a half from shore, but there were no bodies.

There was no escaping the truth. Roberto Clemente was dead. The Great One, *El Magnifico*, had perished trying to keep poor victims from perishing in a small country thousands of miles away. That was the kind of person Roberto was.

Across Puerto Rico, and back in Pittsburgh, and all across the mainland, word of the tragedy filtered back in different ways at different times.

Orlando Cepeda was at his brother's house in Puerto Rico that night. Cepada had been Roberto's bat boy with the Santurce Crabbers and was now a major league star. A chill went down his back as he heard the news. His first thought was that Roberto Clemente cannot die. His second was to remember that Roberto had asked him to come along on that flight.

Pitcher Steve Blass, the World Series hero and Roberto's close friend, was having a party at his house in Pittsburgh. One other player and his wife were still there when the call came in the middle of the night. A plane crash in Puerto Rico. Roberto Clemente was on it. Like Cepeda, Blass thought, *No, Roberto cannot die. He plays as long as he wants to and then becomes governor of Puerto Rico!* The players drove to the house of the Pirates' manager, Joe Brown, where they talked about Roberto all night. They told stories, and laughed and cried. Soon they joined Willie Stargell, and went to the home of announcer Bob Prince, who had planned to have a party that day. The gathering went on, but it became a wake for the team's lost brother, Roberto.

Pirate owner John Galbreath issued a statement. "If you have to die, how better could your death be exemplified than by being on a mission of mercy?"

Vera Clemente stood at the oceanside for days, sometimes looking for him through binoculars. She could scarcely believe what had happened. Later she said, "The whole thing is like a dream to me. I keep thinking he is coming back. I know he's not, though."

The Coast Guard moved from a rescue to a salvage operation. There was no hope of finding anyone alive. The Coast Guard officer pointed out that in such salty water, bodies disintegrated fast. And the waters there were full of sharks.

Still, they did find the body of pilot Jerry Hill. It floated to the surface, completely shattered by the impact. The condition of Hill's body was proof that nobody aboard that plane could have survived the impact once it hit the water.

Nobody knows what happened to the remains of Roberto Clemente. Later plans to make further attempts to recover what was left of the plane were vetoed by the Clemente family.

Thousands of Puerto Ricans tied black ribbons to their automobile antennas. Others went out on small boats and strewed flowers over the crash site.

On January 4, 1973, a special memorial Mass for Roberto Clemente was held at San Fernando Church in Carolina, where Vera and Roberto Clemente had been married eight years earlier. Baseball Commissioner Bowie Kuhn, Joseph Brown and John Galbreath of the Pittsburgh Pirates management, and dozens of members of the Pirates club attended the service. The forty-five-minute Mass included a eulogy by Steve Blass. Throngs of weeping people filled the streets around the church.

On January 14, at Hiram Bithorn Stadium, another requiem Mass was held for Clemente. In New York City, the Mass of the Resurrection was said for him at St. Patrick's Cathedral. President Richard Nixon hailed Clemente "for his splendid qualities as a generous and kind human being."

Shortly after Roberto Clemente's death, plans were underway to hold a special Baseball Hall of Fame election. Ordinarily a player could not be inducted into the Hall of Fame until his playing career had been over for five years. However, in 1939, this rule was suspended when Yankee superstar Lou Gehrig was terminally ill with amyotrophic lateral sclerosis, which has come to be known as "Lou Gehrig's Disease." He was inducted into the Hall of Fame before his death, waiving the rules.

On March 20, 1973, Roberto Clemente received an overwhelming majority of the votes needed to become a member of the Hall of Fame. We all remembered that back in 1968, Roberto Clemente had toured the Baseball Hall of Fame at Cooperstown. Roberto was so modest he didn't say it outright, but he had to have been thinking about his future place in Cooperstown. Everybody knew he'd get in. None of us expected it would be so soon.

On August 6, 1973, Pirate officials and Clemente family members stood as witnesses as Roberto Clemente became the first Latino American player inducted into the Hall of Fame. Inducted alongside of him was his childhood idol, Monte Irvin. The plaque by Roberto's name listed some of his accomplishments: 3,000 hits, leading the National League in batting four times, four seasons with 200 or more hits, a lifetime average of .317, 240 home runs, a Most Valuable Player Award in 1966, and batting .362 in two World Series while hitting safely in all 14 games.

In San Juan, Puerto Rico, the San Juan Coliseum was renamed *Coliseo Roberto Clemente.* A baseball stadium in Carolina, his childhood neighborhood, was named Estadio Roberto Clemente. This stadium contains a striking cenotaph close to the street. It is thirty feet long and seven and one half feet high. The sculptor created three panels illustrating the life of Roberto Clemente. On the far left panel, Roberto is a baby in his mother's arms while his father is working in the nearby cane fields. In the far right panel, he is being honored for his 3,000th baseball hit. In the background his widow holds the National League Hall of Fame plaque, while the figure of death looms over an unquiet ocean. It is in the center panel where the spirit of Roberto Clemente is captured most beautifully. Roberto is shown visiting hospitals, consoling the sick, and standing regal and alone, a lamb in his arms. Everyone was reminded that the name Clemente in Spanish means "merciful."

Throughout Puerto Rico and in the United States, honors flowed in. In Miami, Florida, a Roberto Clemente Park was dedicated in a Hispanic neighborhood. Pittsburgh renamed the Sixth Street Bridge for him. A statue of Roberto stands outside PNC Park in Pittsburgh.

Numerous American schools, streets and parks have been named for Roberto Clemente.

In 1973, Roberto Clemente was posthumously awarded the Congressional Gold Medal. In 2002 he was awarded the Presidential Medal of Freedom and was inducted into the United States Marine Corps Sports Hall of Fame. On August 17, 1984, on the day that would have been Roberto Clemente's fiftieth birthday, the United States Postal system issued a stamp in his honor. In 1999, Roberto Clemente was number 20 in *Sporting News*'s list of the greatest baseball players of all time.

On July 11, 2006, at the major league All-Star Game in Pittsburgh, many of the players on both sides wore wristbands with the initials RCW, standing for Roberto Clemente Walker. (According to Puerto Rican custom, Roberto had two last names. "Walker" was his mother's maiden name.)

Of all the high awards Roberto Clemente received, perhaps the highest was one that he never himself received. In 1971, major league baseball started giving an award called "The Commissioner's Award," to the player who best combined great baseball skill, personal character, and charitable contribution to his community. In its first year, the award went to Willie Mays. After Roberto died, they did not merely give him the award; they *named the award for him.* Now the

Roberto Clemente Award is one of the highest honors a baseball player can ever achieve. Over the years the winners have included such standouts as Brooks Robinson, Cal Ripkin, Kirby Puckett, Ozzie Smith, and Roberto's old friend Willie Stargell.

Vera Clemente raised her three boys in Puerto Rico. When asked why she never remarried, her oldest son said, "In her mind she still loves my dad. She fell in love once and that was it." Then he added, "She is a saint."

Roberto Clemente had the dream of building a Sports City in Puerto Rico, and that dream has been fulfilled by his family and friends. Vera Clemente dedicated herself to working for the dream. Roberto had spent a lot of time looking for just the right piece of land on which to build his sports center. It turned out to be 304 acres of wetland now called *La Ciudad Deportiva Roberto Clemente*. Here would be the Sports City Roberto dreamed of, funded by the government and private donations.

Vera Clemente is president of the Sports City, and her sons are very active. There are seven baseball fields, four professional tennis courts, a swimming pool with ramps for the disabled, a running track, and volleyball and basketball facilities. There are also Tae Kwon Do, summer camp, and social and cultural events. Fairs and auto shows are held there. It is a wonderful place for young people imbued with the spirit of Roberto Clemente. Thousands of children have benefited from the programs and continue to benefit.

As Roberto hoped, the center has also enriched the major leagues with players that might never have had the chance otherwise. It has turned out such major league stars as Benito Santiago, Ruben Sierra, Juan Gonzalez, Carlos Baerga, the Alomar brothers, and Ivan Rodriguez.

Roberto Clemente's eldest son, Robertito, spent three seasons in the minor leagues and then in 1984 played for the Philadelphia Phillies. Knee and back injuries ended his career in 1989. He now works in the Sports Center and has fulfilled another of his father's dreams by doing something for the children of Pittsburgh. In tribute to his father's love for the fans of Pittsburgh, especially the youngsters, he established the Roberto Clemente Foundation in Pittsburgh. Its mission is to provide neighborhood children with after-school tutoring in academic subjects and the opportunity to learn, enjoy and participate in all kinds of sports. Like many large cities, Pittsburgh has gangs, drug problems and the ever-present danger of drive-by shootings. The Foundation rehabilitates local parks, ball fields, and playgrounds, and provides volunteer staff. Like his father, Roberto Clemente, Jr. enjoys working with young people.

Luis Clemente also played baseball with the Pittsburgh Pirates, but tendinitis ended his career. An accomplished musician, he also spends much of his time assisting at the Clemente Sports City and at Boys and Girls Clubs. Enrique never played baseball, but also is active in carrying out his father's good works.

It was one of Roberto Clemente's dreams to make the baseball world aware of the gifts of Hispanic players. Every time he won a title or an award, he hoped to advance that perception. By 1997, forty-two Puerto Ricans were in the major leagues. More than 20 percent of all players are now Hispanic, including Roberto Clemente's nephew, Edward Velazquez of the Colorado Rockies. As a tribute to his uncle, Velazquez played one season under the name Edgard Clemente.

One of the most poignant incidents of the influence of Roberto on the world he left behind too soon is what happened in the small Nicaraguan village of *La Reforma*. Buried in poverty and living in shacks, the five hundred residents of the village had one overriding problem. No matter what happened, illness or accident, they had no access to medical treatment. None had cars, and there was no medical clinic close enough to do them any good.

The Pittsburgh Rotary Club heard of the plight of the people of *La Reforma,* so they adopted the village as a project. They would build a medical facility there. When donations were requested, they came in at a disappointing trickle. Somebody remembered then that at the Pittsburgh Pirates games there is nothing that brings louder applause than clips of Clemente in the glory days. So the Rotary Club said the clinic would be named in honor of Clemente. Money poured in, and in March 1998, the Roberto Clemente Medical Clinic was dedicated in *La Reforma*, Nicaragua. More than twenty-five years after his death, Roberto's legacy of good deeds had once more been used to improve the lives of the poor he loved. Roberto once said, "I would like to be remembered as a player who gave all he had to give." He is now and will always be remembered as a man who gave all he had to give, including his own life, for others.

Of all the awards and honors and remembrances, the one I remember best came just after he died. Up on one of the big hills of Pittsburgh, there's a huge sign in lights that usually has advertising on it. You can see it from all over town. In those first terrible weeks of January back in 1972, when we all were still stunned, I used to take comfort looking up at that sign. It seemed to say everything in two simple words. The sign that blazed out over the Pittsburgh night said, "*Adios Amigo.*"